R. A. WALDRON

The Marconi Company Limited

WAVES AND OSCILLATIONS

Published for
The Commission on College Physics

D. VAN NOSTRAND COMPANY, INC.

Princeton, New Jersey

Toronto　　　　　*London*　　　　*New York*

D. VAN NOSTRAND COMPANY, INC.
120 Alexander St., Princeton, New Jersey
(*Principal Office*)
24 West 40 Street, New York 18, New York

D. VAN NOSTRAND COMPANY, LTD.
358, Kensington High Street, London, W.14, England

D. VAN NOSTRAND COMPANY (Canada), LTD.
25 Hollinger Road, Toronto 16, Canada

PRINTED IN THE UNITED STATES OF AMERICA

Preface

As a small child I used to play with water waves in the bath. As I grew older I learned more about waves, and I am still learning. There is no end to the study, for there are so many kinds of waves, and there is so much to be learned about each of them. They still fascinate me!

The study of waves is essentially mathematical, and it has not been possible to avoid using some mathematics in this book, although it has been kept as simple as possible. Where it is necessary to use sophisticated concepts, mathematical detail and rigor have been cast overboard in favor of qualitative descriptions. It is hoped that, having learned in this book of the existence of certain mathematical techniques, readers will be sufficiently interested to look elsewhere for information about the techniques themselves.

Waves can be studied at a highly sophisticated mathematical level, or wondered over when watching the sea from the top of a cliff, or when idly throwing stones into a pond, or at a railway station when an engine bashes a line of cars. In this little book, I have tried to describe some of the facts about waves and the relationships between various kinds of waves, particularly the latter, which have captured my imagination. It is not possible to do full justice to the subject in a book of this size, but in any case this is not what I wanted to do. Rather than present a cut-and-dried exposition, my aim has been to sketch various topics, and hint at others, and point out cross-connections, in the hope that at least some among my readers will be stimulated to enquire further, and experience for themselves the joys and satisfactions which come as new facts are encountered and deeper understanding is achieved.

R. A. WALDRON

Introduction

This book, as its title indicates, is concerned with waves and oscillations, and the emphasis is on the waves, for oscillations of a resonator can be regarded as superpositions of waves. Before embarking on our discussion, it is helpful to decide just what it is that we are going to discuss—in brief, what is a wave?

In a sense, of course, everybody knows what a wave is. The word, or its equivalents in other languages, exists in the vocabulary of every child. As small children, we have all played with water waves, and with waves on strings. In these cases, we can actually see the waves, and in a concrete, down-to-earth, everyday sense we know very well what we mean by the word. However, when we get a little older, we learn that sound is conveyed to our ears by means of waves, and that our radios detect radio waves. We cannot see radio waves and sound waves; we cannot be aware of them, as waves, in the same way that we are aware of water waves and waves on strings. We also learn that light consists of waves, but there is no obvious connection between waves and the sensation of vision. What is it, then, about the propagation of radio waves, of light, of sound, that leads us to refer to them as waves?

Firstly, let us note that in no case are we directly aware of a wave. We do not, contrary to our first impression, see water waves. We see only water, with its surface arranged in a certain way. Take away the water, and the waves do not remain. Similarly, we can be aware of the motion of a string as waves travel on it, but not of the waves themselves. Thus it does not seem so strange that we cannot be directly aware of light, sound, or radio waves.

We recognize the existence of water waves by observations that we make, not on the waves, but on the water; we see the crests and troughs, regularly spaced, and the distance between successive crests, which we call the wavelength, appears as a property of the wave motion, as does also the speed with which the crests and troughs travel over the surface of the water. Radio waves are not so evident to our senses, but we can detect such properties as wavelength and velocity in them by means of special apparatus. So, too, for light and sound waves. Now, quantities such as wavelengths and velocities readily lend themselves to mathematical operations; lengths can be doubled or halved, or compared with other lengths, or divided by velocities to give times. From studies of waves, a vast store of mathematical knowledge has come, and since the mathematics deals not with waves themselves, nor with the media in which they propagate, but with such quantities as wavelength and velocity—typical wave properties—the kind of mathematics is the same for all kinds of waves.

We thus come to the answer to our question, "What is a wave?" A wave is something that can be treated by wave mathematics!

Certain physical concepts also attach to waves. We have already mentioned velocity and wavelength, and others will be introduced in the course of this book. Mathematics enables us to express relations between the various concepts, so that if certain quantities are measured, others, not so easily accessible to measurement, can be calculated. Sometimes, a quantity is not accessible to measurement at all—for example, the phase velocity of de Broglie waves discussed in section 12. For this reason, it is not advisable to define waves by their possession of certain measurable properties. If a knowledge of phase velocity were regarded as essential, we should say that de Broglie waves are not waves. But those properties that can be measured are wave properties, and they can be treated by wave mathematics.

A certain amount of mathematics is inevitable in discussing waves, but this will be kept to a minimum. Our purpose is to point out the common features of and analogies between waves of different kinds, and no deep study will be made of any particular kind of wave.

Table of Contents

Plates (following p. 24)

1   *Elementary Concepts*

§1. An oscillation is some kind of event, or series of events, which occurs repeatedly, the time interval being the same between any two successive repetitions of a particular event in the series. One of the simplest kinds of motion is *simple harmonic motion;* this is a purely geometrical concept, and as such can be discussed without reference to any particular physical system, but many physical systems perform motions which are essentially simple harmonic.

Consider a point P which moves on a circle with constant angular velocity ω radians per second. In a time t the radius vector rotates through an angle ωt (Fig. 1-1). Draw a perpendicular from P onto the diameter AB, meeting AB in Q. Let OR be drawn perpendicular to AB, and let P start from R at time $t = 0$. Then Q starts from O, moving upwards as P moves to A. P and Q coincide at A when $\omega t = \pi/2$ radians. As P continues to B, Q moves back through O to B, and at time $t = 3\pi/2\omega$, P and Q coincide at B. P continues round the circle to R, which it reaches just as Q reaches O, when $\omega t = 2\pi$. The whole cycle of events then repeats itself indefinitely. The time taken for a complete cycle is $\tau = 2\pi/\omega$; this is called the *periodic time*, or *period*. The motion repeats itself once in time τ, and the quantity $1/\tau$ is called the *frequency* of the oscillations, ν. Since $\omega = 2\pi/\tau$, ω is 2π times the frequency.

The motion of the point Q is called *simple harmonic motion*. At the time t the distance OQ, which is called the *displacement* of Q, is $\xi = a \sin \omega t$, where a is the radius of the circle, OA; a is called the *amplitude* of the motion. The angular distance ωt through which the radius vector is displaced from OR is the *phase* of the motion at the instant t. According to Fig. 1-1, the phase is zero at $t = 0$. But we can measure the phase from any arbitrary position of P, such as S (Fig. 1-2). The distance OQ is now $a \sin P\hat{O}R$, i.e., $\xi = a \sin (\omega t + \alpha_0)$. The phase is now $\varphi = \omega t + \alpha_0$, and at $t = 0$, it is $\varphi_0 = \alpha_0$; this is called the *initial phase*.

1

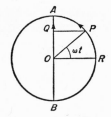 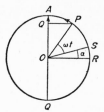

(Left) FIG. 1-1   Simple harmonic motion. (Right) FIG. 1-2   Simple harmonic motion with inital phase α.

The velocity and acceleration of the point Q are given by differentiation. We have

$$\xi = a \sin (\omega t + \alpha_0) \tag{1-1}$$

$$\frac{d\xi}{dt} = a\omega \cos (\omega t + \alpha_0) \tag{1-2}$$

$$\frac{d^2\xi}{dt^2} = -a\omega^2 \sin (\omega t + \alpha_0) \tag{1-3}$$

From equations 1-1 and 1-3,

$$d^2\xi/dt^2 = -\omega^2\xi \tag{1-4}$$

In equation 1-4, which is the differential equation of simple harmonic motion, a and α_0 have been eliminated. The velocity of Q at any instant is the component of the linear velocity of P in the direction parallel to OA, i.e., in the x direction. When P is at R and Q is at O, the linear velocity of P is in the x direction, and the velocity of Q is equal to the total linear velocity of P. Clearly, this is the maximum velocity of Q. When P and Q are at A, the component of linear velocity of P parallel to OA is zero, and Q's velocity is zero. This behavior is described mathematically by equations 1-1 and 1-2, for when $\omega t + \alpha_0$ is zero (or π, 2π, 3π, etc.), $\xi = 0$ and $d\xi/dt = \pm a\omega$. Since the maximum numerical value of the cosine of an angle is 1, this is evidently a maximum velocity. When $\omega t + \alpha_0$ is $\pi/2$ (or $3\pi/2$, $5\pi/2$, etc.), $\cos (\omega t + \alpha_0) = 0$ and the velocity is zero, while $\sin (\omega t + \alpha_0) = \pm 1$ and $\xi = \pm a$—the displacement is a maximum.

§ 2. Physically, simple harmonic motion is the motion of a body which is constrained to move in a straight line, subject to a restoring force which is proportional to the displacement. Thus the restoring force always acts towards the equilibrium point (O in Figs. 1-1 and 1-2), and is zero as the body passes through the equilibrium point. It is a maximum or zero when the displacement is a maximum or zero, respectively, and since the acceleration is proportional to the force, it follows that the acceleration is also a maximum or zero when the displacement is a maximum or zero, respectively. Equations 1-1 and 1-3 show that this is so. The minus sign in equation 1-3 means that the acceleration is oppositely directed to the displacement; when the displacement is upwards, the acceleration is downwards.

One example of simple harmonic motion is provided by a small body of mass m, suspended on a spring or elastic cord of negligible mass (Fig. 1-3). Suppose that the natural length of the cord is L, and that with the weight attached to its end the length becomes $L + l$. The cord is now under a tension equal to the weight of the body. Assuming that the cord obeys Hooke's law, the tension is κl, l being the elastic modulus of the cord. We have

$$\kappa l = mg \tag{1-5}$$

If the body m is displaced from its equilibrium position O, it experiences a force directed towards O, equal to the difference of its weight and the tension of the cord. When the displacement is ξ (positive ξ being measured downwards, so that an increase in ξ means an increase in the length of the cord), the restoring force is thus

$$mg - \kappa(l + \xi) = -\kappa\xi$$

The acceleration is therefore

$$d^2\xi/dt^2 = -\kappa\xi/m \tag{1-6}$$

Comparing equations 1-4 and 1-6, we see that $\omega^2 = \kappa/m$, so that the frequency is

$$\nu = \frac{1}{2\pi} \sqrt{\frac{\kappa}{m}} \tag{1-7}$$

Thus the stiffer the cord, or the smaller the mass of the body, the higher the frequency.

The amplitude and initial phase do not appear in this discussion; the values of these will depend on the way in which the body is set in motion by the experimenter. The frequency of the motion is determined entirely by the nature of the oscillating system—the elastic modulus of the cord and the mass of the body. But its amplitude and initial phase are decided arbitrarily by the experimenter. This fact is echoed in the mathematics of the motion, for equation 1-6 can be solved to give, analogously to equation 1-1,

$$\xi = a \sin (t\sqrt{\kappa/m} + \alpha_0) \tag{1-8}$$

in which a and α_0 are the *arbitrary constants* of the integration.

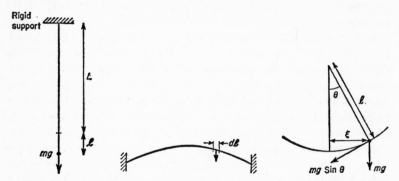

(Left) FIG. 1-3　Vibrating weight supported by elastic cord. (Center) FIG. 1-4　Vibrating string. (Right) FIG. 1-5　Simple pendulum.

Another example of simple harmonic motion is the motion of an element of a stretched string, clamped rigidly at its ends, when the string is vibrating in, say, its lowest mode. At any instant, the string will be in the form shown in Fig. 1-4, and an element such as dl will experience a resultant force in the direction indicated by the arrow, towards the equilibrium position, the force being proportional to the distance of the element from its equilibrium position. A third important example is the motion of the bob of a simple pendulum (Fig. 1-5). The displacement is $\xi = l \sin \theta$, and the restoring force is $mg \sin \theta = mg\xi/l$. As long as θ remains small, the restoring force acts approximately horizontally, and the motion is approximately linear. The restoring force is then proportional to the displacement, and the motion is simple harmonic. The frequency is

$$\nu = \frac{1}{2\pi} \sqrt{\frac{g}{l}} \tag{1-9}$$

and thus is dependent only on the acceleration due to gravity and the length of the string, not on the mass of the bob.

Substituting into equation 1-7 from equation 1-5,

$$\nu = \frac{1}{2\pi}\sqrt{\frac{g}{l}}$$

Comparing this with equation 1-9, we see that a simple pendulum has the same frequency as an elastic cord carrying a weight, if the extension of the cord due to the weight is equal to the length of the pendulum. Surprisingly, the mass of the weight and the properties of the cord do not affect this result.

In the above examples there has been an actual body, possessing mass, which has been moving in space; the displacement has been what we normally mean by a displacement—a departure in geometrical space from a given position. But a periodic phenomenon may be called simple harmonic even though there is no massive body; the motion of the spot of light on the scale of a ballistic galvanometer, for example, is simple harmonic. Again, it is not necessary that the quantity behaving according to equation 1-4 should be a distance. In the case of electromagnetic waves, for example, it is a component of electric or magnetic field.

§ 3. The relation of simple harmonic motion to wave motion can be brought out by plotting the distance OQ in Fig. 1-2 as a function of time. This is illustrated in Fig. 1-6, where t is plotted along a

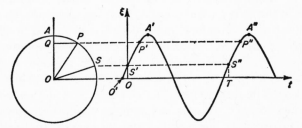

FIG. 1-6   Displacement as a function of time for simple harmonic motion.

horizontal axis, and ξ parallel to a vertical axis. The point P' is obtained by drawing a horizontal line through P to the required value of t. The point obtained traces out the curve shown as P travels

round the circle. The distance between corresponding points on the
wavy curve, such as P' and P'', S' and S'', or A' and A'', is the periodic time τ. The curve is a plot of equation 1-1, and is a sine wave.

The curve

$$\xi = a \sin (\beta z + \alpha') \qquad (1\text{-}10)$$

which is shown in Fig. 1-7, is a sine wave again, and analogously
to Fig. 1-6 and equation 1-1, the phase at $z = 0$ is α'. Now suppose
that the curve of Fig. 1-7 is moved as a whole in the z direction with

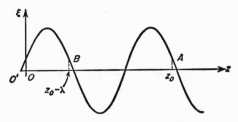

FIG. 1-7   Propagation of a wave.

constant velocity v; let us consider the value of ξ at a point $z = z_0$,
at various times. Suppose that equation 1-10 holds at the time $t = 0$,
and suppose that after a time τ the phase at z_0 has changed by 2π.
At time τ, then, we have

$$\xi = a \sin (\beta z_0 + \alpha' - 2\pi)$$

and at any other time we shall have

$$\xi = a \sin (\beta z_0 + \alpha' - 2\pi t/\tau)$$

But $2\pi t/\tau = 2\pi \nu t = \omega t$. Hence

$$\xi = a \sin (\beta z_0 + \alpha' - \omega t) \qquad (1\text{-}11)$$

The minus sign appears before ωt because at $t = 0$ the point A co-
incides with z_0, while after time τ the point B has moved up to
occupy the position initially held by A. The phase of B is 2π less
than that of A, i.e., as t increases, the phase of z_0 decreases. The
above argument holds whatever may be the value of z_0. Thus more
generally we may write

$$\xi = a \sin (\beta z - \omega t + \alpha) \qquad (1\text{-}12)$$

where α represents any arbitrary phase angle.

The distance between two successive corresponding points such as A and B in Fig. 1-7 is called the *wavelength*, λ, of the wave. Between them, the phase changes by 2π. Hence $\beta\lambda = 2\pi$, i.e.,

$$\beta = 2\pi/\lambda \qquad (1\text{-}13)$$

β is called the *phase constant* of the wave. The velocity of the wave is given by the distance traveled in a certain time by the curve of Fig. 1-7, which is called the *wave profile*. In time τ, the wave progresses by one wavelength, λ, so that the velocity v is λ/τ. It is often more convenient to work in terms of β and ω, and putting $\lambda = 2\pi/\beta$ and $\tau = 2\pi/\omega$, we obtain $v = \omega/\beta$. The velocity so given is called the *phase velocity* to distinguish it from the group velocity which we shall meet in § 8. We shall denote the phase velocity by v_φ. Thus

$$v_\varphi = \omega/\beta \qquad (1\text{-}14)$$

We can now substitute for ω from equation 1-14 into equation 1-12, which becomes

$$\xi = a \sin\left[\beta(z - v_\varphi t) + \alpha\right] \qquad (1\text{-}15)$$

Comparing equations 1-15 and 1-10, it is seen that ξ may be regarded as a function of $(z - v_\varphi t)$.

Let us now imagine ourselves to be observing a wave passing a given point. Then z is a constant, and so, therefore, is βz, which can be regarded as part of the initial phase for the point in question. Putting $\alpha + \beta z = \varphi$, equation 1-12 becomes

$$\xi = a \sin\left(-\omega t + \varphi\right) \quad \text{or} \quad \xi = -a \sin\left(\omega t - \varphi\right)$$

which becomes identical with equation 1-1 if $\varphi = -\alpha_0 \pm n\pi$ (n an integer). Thus if the wave consists in vibrations of particles, the individual particles perform simple harmonic motion. Since the initial phase includes βz, the phases of the particles differ from one to another as one goes along in the z direction.

Alternatively, we can consider equation 1-12 at an instant of time. Then ωt can be taken as constant, and equation 1-12 becomes identical with 1-10 if $\alpha' = \alpha - \omega t$. Thus equation 1-12 gives the motion of an individual particle at all times at any point on the z axis, or the positions of the particles at all sites along the z axis at any instant of time.

As a physical illustration of this, consider a piece of thin rope of

some length, lying flat and straight on the ground. Take one end
in the hand and move it up and down regularly. The motion of the
end of the rope imitates the motion of the point Q in Fig. 1-6. The
displacement moves out along the rope as a wave, and at any instant
the distance reached along the rope by a particular portion of the
wave profile depends on the time that has elapsed since it left the
end. Thus distance along the rope may be regarded as the time axis,
and the form of the rope at any instant gives the curve of Fig. 1-6.
Alternatively, we can think of the situation as it really is, and a
photograph of the rope at any instant will show the wave profile as
in Fig. 1-7.

Another important point may be brought out here, although it is
a digression from the present discussion. Any point in the rope is
performing simple harmonic motion as the wave progresses (assuming that the motion imparted to the end is described by equation
1-1). This illustrates the general principle that a wave of any type
can be generated by exciting, at some point in the wave field, just
that motion which is proper to the wave. Disturbances will then
radiate outwards from that point, and there will be an initial period
when all sorts of waves are present. Gradually, however, all waves
will die out except that one to which the form of excitation is proper.
This is a most important point, and we shall return to it in §§ 32
and 59.

§ 4. In equation 1-12, the displacement ξ is given as a function
of two variables, z and t; in other words, the position of a particle
with respect to its equilibrium point depends on the site of its equilibrium point on the z axis, and on the time. It is possible to differ-
entiate ξ with respect to z, regarding t as constant, or with respect
to t, regarding z as constant. This process is called partial differentiation. Differentiating in the left-hand column with respect to z and
in the right-hand column with respect to t, we proceed analogously
to equations 1-1, 1-2, 1-3, and 1-4, obtaining

$$\frac{\partial \xi}{\partial t} = -\omega a \cos (\beta z - \omega t + \alpha) \qquad \frac{\partial \xi}{\partial z} = \beta a \cos (\beta z - \omega t + \alpha)$$

$$\frac{\partial^2 \xi}{\partial t^2} = -\omega^2 a \sin (\beta z - \omega t + \alpha) \qquad \frac{\partial^2 \xi}{\partial z^2} = -\beta^2 a \sin (\beta z - \omega t + \alpha)$$

$$\text{i.e.,} \quad \partial^2 \xi / \partial t^2 = -\omega^2 \xi \qquad \qquad \partial^2 \xi / \partial z^2 = -\beta^2 \xi$$

Eliminating ξ,
$$\partial^2\xi/\partial z^2 = (\beta^2/\omega^2)\cdot\partial^2\xi/\partial t^2$$

In these equations, ∂ is written instead of d to denote a *partial* differential coefficient. Using equation 1-14, we obtain

$$\frac{\partial^2\xi}{\partial z^2} = \frac{1}{v_\varphi^2}\frac{\partial^2\xi}{\partial t^2} \qquad (1\text{-}16)$$

Equation 1-16 is a very important partial differential equation. It is called the *wave equation in one dimension*, and is obeyed by all waves, whatever may be their amplitude, phase, or frequency. The nature of the wave (sound wave, electromagnetic wave, etc.) gives meaning to v_φ and ξ, but does not affect the form of the wave equation.

Equation 1-16 can be integrated. We shall not go through the steps, but the reader may like to verify by differentiation that the equation

$$\xi = f(z - v_\varphi t) \qquad (1\text{-}17)$$

is a solution of equation 1-16 for any function f of the variable $z - v_\varphi t$. Equation 1-15 is a special case of this. We have assumed v_φ to be constant; what happens when v_φ is not constant (i.e., when there is dispersion) will be considered in § 8.

§ 5. In the case of the waves on a free rope, mentioned at the end of § 3, the displacement ξ is in the vertical plane, while the motion of the wave is along the rope in the horizontal direction. Thus ξ is perpendicular to z—it lies in the *transverse plane*. In many other forms of wave motion, the displacement is perpendicular to the direction of propagation; examples are waves on strings, electromagnetic waves, flexural waves on bars and plates, and many others. Such waves are called *transverse waves*. In other waves, the motion is longitudinal, i.e., ξ is in the z direction, and the waves are called *longitudinal waves*. A particularly important example of this is the case of sound waves; tidal waves (§ 7) also approximate to longitudinal waves.

The motions of particles are not necessarily simple harmonic. In water waves of the surface variety (ripples on the surface of a pond), for example, the particles of water move in circles. Figure 1-8 shows the paths of particles at intervals along the propagation direction,

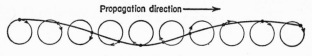

FIG. 1-8   Water wave.

and the positions of particles are indicated by the dots. The curve joining the dots gives the wave profile. The propagation direction lies in the plane of the circles. Another example is that of the circularly polarized electromagnetic wave (§ 11).

§ 6. Many common types of wave propagate in material bodies, and it is now convenient to discuss these briefly in the light of the foregoing theory. When a wave passes through a medium, the particles of the medium perform some sort of periodic motion. The motion of one particle influences its neighbors, which in turn influence their neighbors, and in this way the wave progresses. In the case of waves on a string, the transverse motion of a particle of the string necessarily drags the remainder of the string with it. Figure 1-9(a) shows a single wavelength of a string on which a wave is propagating. The string at P is at its equilibrium position and is moving downwards at maximum (negative) velocity. At Q the element of string has reached its maximum displacement and is instantaneously at rest before starting to move downwards. At R the string is moving upwards with maximum positive velocity. The velocity of the string is illustrated in Fig. 1-9(b). Where the displacement is sinusoidal, the velocity is cosinusoidal (cf. equations 1-1, 1-2, 1-12); velocity and displacement differ in phase by $\pi/2$.

A short time before the time represented by Fig. 1-9, the point P had a small positive displacement. Similarly, after another short time has elapsed, P' will have its displacement reduced to zero. The element of string at P' is dragged along by that at P in its downward motion, by virtue of the connecting string PP', and in this way the wave propagates along the string.

In order for a wave to be able to propagate on a string, the string must be under tension. When an element of string, at some point such as S (Fig. 1-9(a)), is displaced, it is subject to tension forces pulling with equal strength but not quite opposite directions. The resultant force acts towards the equilibrium position and forms

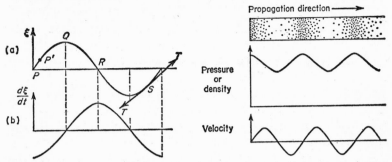

(Left) FIG. 1-9 Traveling wave on a string. (Right) FIG. 1-10 Sound waves in air. The particle velocity is positive for a particle moving in the propagation direction.

the restoring force. In order to displace the string, work is done against the restoring force, and the string therefore possesses potential energy. It also possesses kinetic energy by virtue of its transverse velocity. At P, the potential energy is zero and the kinetic energy a maximum. At Q, the kinetic energy is zero and the potential energy is a maximum. In general, an element of the string will possess both potential and kinetic energy, and the total energy will be constant. As the wave flows past a point, the energy is continually changing from the kinetic form to the potential and back again.

This is an example of an important feature of all waves. There are always two quantities which differ in phase by $\pi/2$, and it is not always meaningful to try to decide which of them is to be called the displacement, when neither of them is an actual shift in position. Associated with each quantity is a form of energy, and the energy at a point through which the wave travels is continuously changing backwards and forwards from one form to the other. At the same time, energy is being carried along by the wave.

In the case of sound waves, the periodically-varying quantities are the pressure or density of an elementary volume in a mass of gas, and the velocity with which the elementary volume moves. This is illustrated in Fig. 1-10. The top diagram, in which the densities of the dots indicate the densities of the gas, shows the actual situation in a gas at some instant—rather exaggerated, for the minimum density is not actually zero. Rather, the densities indicated in the diagram should be regarded as superimposed on a steady density which is not shown. The pressure or density (since pressure is proportional to density) and the velocity of the gas molecules are also indicated graphically. In accordance with what was said above, the density and velocity differ in phase by $\pi/2$. At a point such as P, for example, the molecules have flowed in from either side. Now that the density is a maximum, there is no more flow—the velocity is zero. The energy of the wave exists partly as the kinetic energy of the moving gas molecules and partly as the potential energy of the compressed gas. When the kinetic energy at a point is zero, further compression ceases, and the gas then starts to expand. As it does so, neighboring gas molecules are accelerated, at the expense of the potential energy of compression; as the potential energy falls, so does the pressure. There is also a maximum of potential energy at a point of maximum rarefaction, where again the particle velocities, and hence the kinetic energy, are zero. The potential energy is that holding the rest of the gas back, before it rushes in to remove the partial vacuum.

In the case of water waves, particles of water move in circles, as we have seen (§ 5). The velocity is not uniform, however. At the top of its circular path, a particle moves slower than at the bottom, and so has a smaller kinetic energy; the difference of kinetic energies is equal to the extra potential energy that the particle has at the top of its circle.

§ 7. The velocity of motion of the particles of the medium through which a wave travels should not be confused with the velocity of travel of the wave (§ 3, equation 1-14). The velocity of the individual particles depends on the amplitude and frequency of the wave, as can be seen from § 4. This velocity is $d\xi/dt$, and is equal to $a\omega$ times a periodic function of amplitude unity. The maximum value of $d\xi/dt$ is therefore $a\omega$, i.e., the amplitude times 2π times the frequency. (See also Plate I.)

On the other hand, the phase velocity is independent of amplitude, and is governed by the properties of the medium and by its state; the state may be, for example, the pressure of a gas or the tension of a string, while the properties involved are such quantities as density and elasticity. Sometimes the frequency also is involved; we shall return to this point in the next section.

Water waves have a phase velocity given by

$$v_\varphi = \sqrt{\frac{\lambda g}{2\pi} + \frac{2\pi T}{\lambda}} \tag{1-18}$$

where λ is the wavelength, g the acceleration due to gravity, and T the surface tension. When λ is small, only the second term under the square root sign is important, and the waves are called surface waves. The wave motion is confined to a region near the liquid surface, and the particles describe the circular paths already mentioned. When λ is very large, only the first term under the root sign is important, and the waves then consist of the motion backwards and forwards of large masses of water. Such waves are *tidal waves;* their wavelength may be many miles, and their height only a few feet, so that they pass ships at sea unnoticed, but dash onto the shore with great force. Tidal waves, with the rigorous logic of science, have nothing to do with tides, being caused by storms, earthquakes, and other calamities.

For *sound waves in a gas*, the velocity is

$$v_\varphi = \sqrt{\gamma P/\rho} \tag{1-19}$$

where P is the pressure, ρ the density, and γ a constant depending on the gas. Analogously, the phase velocity for *compressional waves in a solid* (such as longitudinal waves traveling along a bar) is

$$v_\varphi = \sqrt{E/\rho} \tag{1-20}$$

where E is Young's modulus; for *sound waves in a liquid*, it is

$$v_\varphi = \sqrt{\gamma \kappa/\rho} \tag{1-21}$$

where κ is the bulk modulus of the liquid; for *torsional waves in a wire* or *bar*, it is

$$v_\varphi = \sqrt{n/\rho} \tag{1-22}$$

where n is the rigidity modulus; and for *transverse waves* (*flexural waves*) *on a string* it is

$$v_\varphi = \sqrt{T/m} \tag{1-23}$$

where T is the tension and m the mass per unit length.

§ 8. If the properties of a medium, or its state, are dependent on frequency, the phase velocity is not a constant. Equation 1-14 is still true, but the wavelength is not now inversely proportional to frequency. This phenomenon is known as *dispersion;* in the case of light waves, when a beam of white light is passed through a glass prism, the different colors, corresponding to different frequencies, travel in different directions on emerging, i.e., they are dispersed. This is said to be due to the dispersion of the glass, its property of carrying light waves with different phase velocities for different frequencies.

The phenomenon of dispersion is closely related to the rate at which energy is carried by the wave. For the energy does not necessarily travel with the wave at the same velocity as the wavefronts; in fact, the velocities are the same only in rare instances, although they are often very nearly the same. Under certain circumstances, even, the energy can move in a direction opposite to the motion of the wavefronts; such waves are called backward waves (§ 58).

The velocity with which the energy travels is called the *group velocity*, v_g. It may be expressed in a variety of ways; probably the most useful is

$$v_g = d\omega/d\beta \tag{1-24}$$

from which it is readily seen (using equation 1-14 and remembering that $\beta = 2\pi/\lambda$, $\omega = 2\pi\nu$) that

$$v_g = \frac{d\nu}{d(1/\lambda)} = v_\varphi - \lambda \frac{dv_\varphi}{d\lambda} \tag{1-25}$$

In the case of light waves, the velocity of light *in vacuo*, c, is related to the phase velocity v_φ in some other medium by the *refractive index* μ:

$$\mu = c/v_\varphi \tag{1-26}$$

μ is a property of the medium, and in general is frequency-dependent. Then v_φ is also frequency-dependent, and the *dispersion* of the medium may be defined in terms of the frequency-dependence of μ. In fact it is taken as $d\mu/d\lambda$, where λ is the wavelength *in vacuo*, $= c/\nu$. Now,

$$\frac{d\mu}{d\lambda} = \frac{d(c/v_\varphi)}{d\lambda} = \frac{-c}{v_\varphi^2} \frac{dv_\varphi}{d\lambda} \tag{1-27}$$

From equations 1-25 and 1-27,

$$v_g = v_\varphi + \frac{c^2}{\nu\mu^2} \frac{d\mu}{d\lambda} = v_\varphi + \frac{v_\varphi^2}{\nu} \frac{d\mu}{d\lambda} \tag{1-28}$$

This may be written

$$v_g = v_\varphi \left[1 + \frac{v_\varphi}{v} \frac{d\mu}{d\lambda} \right] = v_\varphi \left[1 + \frac{\lambda}{\mu} \frac{d\mu}{d\lambda} \right]$$

$$= \frac{v_\varphi}{1 - \dfrac{\lambda}{\mu} \dfrac{d\mu}{d\lambda}} \qquad \text{if } \frac{\lambda}{\mu} \frac{d\mu}{d\lambda} \ll 1$$

Hence

$$\frac{c}{v_g} = \frac{c}{v_\varphi} \left[1 - \frac{\lambda}{\mu} \frac{d\mu}{d\lambda} \right]$$

i.e.,

$$\frac{c}{v_g} = \mu - \lambda \frac{d\mu}{d\lambda} \qquad (1\text{-}29)$$

Equations 1-28 and 1-29 show the relationship between dispersion and group velocity. From these, as also from equation 1-25, it is seen that when the dispersion is zero, the group velocity is equal to the phase velocity.

The dispersion of a medium, for any kind of wave, is usually negative (i.e., $d\mu/d\lambda < 0$), except in short regions where it is positive. Typical dispersion curves are shown in Fig. 1-11. Where $d\mu/d\lambda$ is positive, this is said to be a region of *anomalous dispersion*.

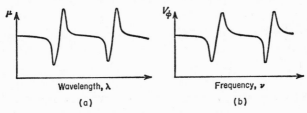

FIG. 1-11   Typical dispersion curves.

§ 9. The waves we have considered so far have been propagated by means of the periodic motions of material particles under the action of a restoring force. The same idea may be extended to the motions of electrons in an electrical conductor in which an alternating current is flowing. It is more convenient, however, to think in terms of voltage and current.

For a circuit containing only resistance, the relation between current and voltage is the same as for direct current. Thus in Fig. 1-12, if I is the instantaneous current in a resistor R when the instantaneous voltage across it is V, we can write, at any instant,

$$V = IR \qquad (1\text{-}30)$$

and if the voltage is varying sinusoidally, we have

$$\left.\begin{array}{l} V = V_0 \sin(\omega t + \varphi) \\ I = I_0 \sin(\omega t + \varphi) \end{array}\right\} \qquad (1\text{-}31)$$

where ω is 2π times the frequency of the generator and φ is a phase angle which is the same for the current as for the voltage, i.e., the current and the voltage are in phase.

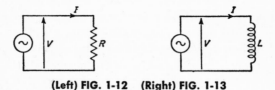

(Left) FIG. 1-12   (Right) FIG. 1-13

If a coil having a very small resistance is connected between the terminals of a battery, a very large direct current flows and the coil burns out. But if it is connected across the terminals of an AC generator, the current is limited, because of the inductance of the coil. This causes an electromotive force to be set up in the coil as the current changes, and this EMF is in the opposite direction to that driving the current. It can be shown that for the circuit of Fig. 1-13, containing a coil of inductance L, the current and applied voltage are related by

$$\left.\begin{array}{c} I = I_0 \sin(\omega t + \varphi - \pi/2); \ V = V_0 \sin(\omega t + \varphi); \\ V_0/I_0 = \omega L \end{array}\right\} \qquad (1\text{-}32)$$

and

This relation between current and voltage is illustrated in Fig. 1-14 for the case $\varphi = 0$; the current lags on the voltage by a quarter-

FIG. 1-14   Voltage and current in the circuit of Fig. 1-13.

cycle, and the ratio of voltage amplitude to current amplitude is proportional to the frequency, unlike the resistor case, where the ratio is constant. The quantity ωL is called the *reactance* of the inductor.

If a circuit contains both an inductor and a resistor, as in Fig. 1-15, the current lags on the voltage by an amount between 0 and $\pi/2$. The relation between current and voltage is

$$\left.\begin{aligned} I &= I_0 \sin \omega t \\ V &= I_0 \sqrt{R^2 + \omega^2 L^2} \sin (\omega t + \alpha) \end{aligned}\right\} \qquad (1\text{-}33)$$

where $\tan \alpha = \omega L / R$. When R becomes zero, this reduces to equation 1-32, and when L is zero, it reduces to equation 1-30. The quantity $\sqrt{R^2 + \omega^2 L^2}$, which is neither a pure resistance nor a pure reactance, is called the *impedance* of the circuit.

When equations 1-31 are differentiated repeatedly, we obtain

$$\frac{dV}{dt} = \omega V_0 \cos (\omega t + \varphi); \frac{d^2V}{dt^2} = -\omega^2 V_0 \sin (\omega t + \varphi)$$

so that

$$\left.\begin{aligned} \frac{d^2V}{dt^2} &= -\omega^2 V \\ \\ \frac{d^2I}{dt^2} &= -\omega^2 I \end{aligned}\right\} \qquad (1\text{-}34)$$

Similarly,

(Left) Fig. 1-15 (Right) FIG. 1-16

These equations are identical in form with equation 1-4, the equation of simple harmonic motion, and the notion of displacement, which in the examples of § 2 meant real displacements of position, is extended here to electrical voltages and currents. Mathematically, then, we can expect such systems as simple pendulums, weights hanging on springs, and alternating-current circuits to behave in analogous ways, so that we can use the behavior of one system to help us to understand another. Electrical engineers, who learn about

AC theory before they learn about waves, usually try to explain everything in terms of AC theory. This one-sided approach to the theory of waves and oscillations is sometimes helpful, but can often limit the understanding rather than advance it. The aim in this book is to try to broaden the reader's outlook so that he will learn to use analogies as a guide, but will not come to depend on them, or on a particular kind of analogy, slavishly.

Another important alternating-current circuit element is the capacitor (Fig. 1-16). This is an open circuit to direct current, but will pass alternating current because electric charge is able to pile up on the plates of the capacitor. The relation between current and voltage is given by

$$V = V_0 \sin (\omega t + \varphi); I = I_0 \sin (\omega t + \varphi + \pi/2) \atop V_0 = I_0/\omega C \Bigg\} \quad (1\text{-}35)$$

and now the current leads the voltage by 90°. Taking φ to be $\pi/2$, V is a maximum at time $t = 0$ and no current flows. The charge on the capacitor is a maximum and gives rise to a voltage on the capacitor which balances the generator voltage V. As V starts to fall, charge leaves the capacitor at an increasing rate, and the current becomes a maximum when V is zero. Current continues to flow as V becomes negative, and becomes zero as V reaches its maximum in the negative sense. As with the inductor, equations 1-34 can be obtained by differentiation.

§ 10.   An important group of waves which we have not considered so far consists of the various kinds of electromagnetic waves. Here again the quantities which appear in the wave equations are not the displacements (of position) of particles; they are components of electric or magnetic field. A particularly simple manner of propagation is the *plane wave*, in which the wave travels in the z direction, and the phase and amplitude are independent of x and y. The electric and magnetic fields lie in the transverse plane and are mutually perpendicular. If their directions are constant, we may take the electric vector E to be in the x direction and the magnetic vector H to be in the y direction. The fields are then

$$E_x = E_0 \sin (\beta z - \omega t) \atop H_y = H_0 \sin (\beta z - \omega t) \Bigg\} \quad (1\text{-}36)$$

For any wave, the ratio of H_0 to E_0 is a constant depending on the properties of the medium. These equations may be compared with equation 1-12.

Electromagnetic fields are not physical entities in the same way that particles and displacements of particles are. They are mathematical concepts by means of which the effects of charges, and motions of charges, on stationary or moving bodies which carry charges, can be calculated. For example, if a body A carries a charge, and if another charged body B is placed near to A, it experiences a repulsion, which can be measured. The repulsion occurs between the charges, and that is all that we can say, physically. However, mathematically it is convenient to imagine A to be surrounded by a field of force, which gives the value of the repulsion at a given point that a body will experience at that point when carrying a unit charge. The field of force is called an electric field and can be treated by potential theory. Similar arguments apply to magnetic fields. Relations between these fields are summarized in Maxwell's famous set of equations, from which a wave equation may be derived. Thus electromagnetic disturbances propagate as waves; as stated in the Introduction, we call them waves because they can be treated by wave mathematics, and such properties as phase, amplitude, wavelength, phase velocity, and group velocity are appropriate. But these waves cannot be directly observed, and their existence is only inferred from their effects. *

Electromagnetic waves are usually divided, for convenience, into a number of kinds, according to the techniques used to study them. The techniques depend on the frequency and wavelength of the waves, and there is a certain amount of overlap, so that there is no sharp division between one kind and the next.

The term *light waves* originally applied only to the visual range, with wavelengths from $4 \cdot 10^{-5}$ cm to $7.2 \cdot 10^{-5}$ cm. Shorter waves, the ultraviolet, and longer waves, the infrared, are now regarded as light waves because they are studied by means of lenses, prisms, and diffraction gratings and detected by the photoelectric effect or pho-

* The wave description of electromagnetic phenomena is only a matter of convention. As long ago as 1908, W. Ritz pointed out that a particle description of electromagnetic phenomena is equally possible. There is a striking similarity between this wave-particle duality and that of the wave mechanics of electrons and other small particles.

tochemically (photoelectric cells, photographic plates and films). Still shorter waves are the X-rays, which can be studied by diffraction effects in crystals and are generated by bombarding metals with beams of electrons. A material can only act as a lens if it appears homogeneous to the wave, i.e., if its grain size is very small compared with a wavelength. X-rays, however, have wavelengths of the order of the dimensions of the unit cells of crystal lattices, so that no material appears homogeneous to them. Lenses for X-rays therefore do not exist, and they are diffracted by the atoms in crystals. This makes them very useful for studying crystal structures.

Energy is emitted from atoms in the form of light rays and X-rays as the energy of electrons in the atoms changes. The electrons in an atom are able to have only certain discrete values of energy, and normally all the lower energy levels are occupied. If one electron somehow acquires an increased energy, it can fall to a lower energy level, and in doing so releases a pulse of energy as light or X-radiation. The increased energy may be obtained, for example, as a result of collisions with other atoms; the hotter the body, the more violent the collisions, and so the greater the likelihood of an atom's obtaining energy which goes to raise an electron to a higher energy level. This is why hot bodies become incandescent. X-rays can be generated by bombarding metals with very high-energy electron beams, which penetrate deep into individual atoms and knock electrons out of very deep energy-levels. A hole is thus left, into which electrons can fall from higher levels; the separation between levels is large, so that high-energy radiation is emitted.

Going to still smaller wavelengths, we have γ rays, which are short pulses of energy ejected from radioactive nuclei. They are generated by changes in the energy of particles in the nucleus, analogously to light and X-radiation. Individual pulses are released, unlike X-rays and light in which there are so many pulses that they appear as continuous beams. The γ rays are studied by their collisions with small particles such as electrons and atomic nuclei, and behave much more like particles than waves. For this reason we shall not discuss them further in this book.

Going to greater wavelengths than those of light, we have first heat waves, i.e., infrared waves which are of too great wavelength to cause photochemical or photoelectric effects, although, as pointed out above, there is no sharp dividing line between light and heat. Heat waves interact with atoms as wholes, rather than with particles within the atom. When heat waves fall on a body, they agitate the atoms, increasing their energy of vibration or translational motion, and thus the temperature of the body is raised. Heat waves are detected by devices in which the temperature of a sensitive element is raised, the increase in temperature being measured. Such instruments are thermocouples, in which the rise in temperature of a junction between two metals is measured by the thermoelectric effect produced, and bolometers, in which the rise in temperature of a thin wire is measured by the change in its electrical resistance. There are also radiometers, in which radiation falls on one surface of one blade at a time of a little paddle wheel, in an envelope of gas at very low pressure. Gas molecules impinging on the hot side of the blade recoil faster than molecules impinging on the cold side, and momentum is conserved by the imparting of motion to the wheel. The motion is not appreciably resisted by the gas because of the low pressure, and the intensity of the radiation can be deduced from the rate of turning of the wheel.

Still longer waves interact with sizable chunks of matter and can be studied much more conveniently because now we can actually make the devices with which the waves interact in machine shops, instead of depending on naturally occurring materials. These waves are known as microwaves and propagate conveniently in metal tubes and other artificial guiding structures. We shall study them in Chapter 5.

At still longer wavelengths, the sizes of practically convenient structures are much smaller than the wavelength. The waves are launched from and received by aerials which are small compared with a wavelength, and might almost be regarded as point sources.

Finally, there have recently been discovered waves whose periodic time is of the order of tens of seconds or minutes, corresponding to wavelengths of many times the diameter, not of the earth itself, but of the region over which the earth's magnetic field is effective. * Not much is known about these waves, but it is believed that they are probably due to interactions between charged particles radiating

* J. R. Heirtzler, "The Longest Electromagnetic Waves," *Scientific American*, Vol. 206, No. 3, pp. 128–137 (March 1962).

from the sun and the earth's magnetic field. They are being studied by essentially DC techniques—highly sensitive magnetometers are used to measure the magnetic field at a point as a function of time. The measurement takes a time small compared with the periodic time, so that the field is approximately constant during a measurement. The amplitudes of the waves are very small, so very sensitive instruments are necessary; measurements of electric field are not possible at present because electrometers of sufficiently high sensitivity do not exist.

§ 11. The waves described by equations 1-36 are said to be *plane polarized*, because the electric vector lies in a single plane. Light rays from the sun or from an electric light bulb or from a candle flame are not polarized in any preferred direction; they can be thought of as consisting of a large number of rays, each polarized in some way, but all polarized differently from each other. Such light is said to be *unpolarized*.

Now let us consider two plane-polarized waves, with their planes of polarization perpendicular to each other, and let us consider the E vectors at a particular point where $z = z_0$. If these differ in phase by $\pi/2$, we have, for one wave,

$$E_x = E_0 \sin (\beta z_0 - \omega t) \tag{1-37}$$

and for the other

$$E_y = E_0' \sin (\beta z_0 - \omega t + \pi/2) = E_0' \cos (\beta z_0 - \omega t) \tag{1-38}$$

The field vectors are illustrated in Fig. 1-17, where it is supposed

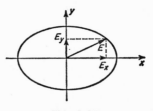

FIG. 1-17

that $E_0' < E_0$. When $\beta z_0 - \omega t = 0$, E_x is zero and E_y is a maximum, equal to E_0'. When $\beta z_0 - \omega t = \pi/2$, $E_x = E_0$ and $E_y = 0$. In general, the resultant E vector is given by

$$E = \sqrt{E_x^2 + E_y^2}$$

$$= \sqrt{E_0^2 \sin^2 (\beta z_0 - \omega t) + E_0'^2 \cos^2 (\beta z_0 - \omega t)} \quad (1\text{-}39)$$

When $E_0' = E_0$, this becomes

$$E = E_0 \sqrt{\sin^2 (\beta z_0 - \omega t) + \cos^2 (\beta z_0 - \omega t)} = E_0 \quad (1\text{-}40)$$

We now have a vector of constant magnitude E_0, which rotates with uniform angular velocity ω, its position at any instant being given by $\beta z_0 - \omega t$.

Equations 1-39 and 1-40 hold for all values of z and may be replaced by

$$E = \sqrt{E_0^2 \sin^2 (\beta z - \omega t) + E_0'^2 \cos^2 (\beta z - \omega t)} \quad (1\text{-}41)$$

and

$$E = E_0 \sqrt{\sin^2 (\beta z - \omega t) + \cos^2 (\beta z - \omega t)} = E_0 \quad (1\text{-}42)$$

Equation 1-42 represents a wave in which the E vector rotates steadily, with constant magnitude, as it progresses in the z direction. If the vector is represented by a line, one end of the line moves straight along the z axis, while the other rotates uniformly, following a helical path. Such a wave is said to be *circularly polarized*. Equation 1-41 represents a similar wave in which the magnitude of the vector, or length of the line, varies periodically as it rotates, as in Fig. 1-17. Such a wave is said to be *elliptically polarized*.

An equation similar to equation 1-39 results from consideration of a particle which performs two simple harmonic motions simultaneously, at right angles, and differing in phase by $\pi/2$. Then, adapting equation 1-1, we have

$$\xi_x = a \sin (\omega t + \alpha_0)$$

$$\xi_y = b \sin (\omega t + \alpha_0 + \pi/2) = b \cos (\omega t + \alpha_0)$$

and the resultant displacement is

$$\xi = \sqrt{\xi_x^2 + \xi_y^2} = \sqrt{a^2 \sin^2 (\omega t + \alpha_0) + b^2 \sin^2 (\omega t + \alpha_0)}$$

If $b = a$, $\xi = a$; the particle is said to perform *circular harmonic motion*. When $b \neq a$, the particle performs *elliptic harmonic motion*.

Only a transverse wave can be plane or circularly polarized, because the polarization depends on there being two orthogonal directions in which the displacement (in its generalized sense) may lie. Thus electromagnetic waves and waves on strings may be polarized. Longitudinal waves, such as sound waves or compressional waves in elastic solids, cannot be polarized because the displacement can lie in only one direction, the longitudinal direction.

§ 12. Surprisingly, it was discovered in the 1920's that beams of small particles such as electrons can exhibit wavelike properties. They are diffracted by crystals in much the same way as X-rays, which have comparable wavelengths. A quantity ψ can be defined, a function of position, such that $|\psi|^2 d\tau$ is the probability that an electron is situated in the volume element $d\tau$. When only one electron exists in a system, ψ is so scaled that the integral of $|\psi|^2 d\tau$ over the volume of the system is unity, i.e., the probability that the electron is somewhere in the system is unity. When there are many electrons, as in a beam from an electron gun, ψ can be scaled in some other convenient way. This scaling is called *normalization*.

The quantity ψ is given as the solution of *Schrödinger's equation:*

$$\left\{\frac{\partial^2}{\partial x^2} + \frac{\partial^2}{\partial y^2} + \frac{\partial^2}{\partial z^2} + \frac{8\pi^2 m}{h^2}(W - V)\right\}\psi = 0 \qquad (1\text{-}43)$$

where m is the mass of the particle in question, W its total energy, and V its potential energy (e.g., the electrostatic energy of an electron in an electric field). The quantity h is known as *Planck's constant* and first came into use at the end of the nineteenth century in connection with statistical theories of heat. Schrödinger's equation may be regarded as equivalent to the fact, found empirically by de Broglie from observations of the diffraction of electrons by crystals, that a beam of particles, all having momentum p, behaves as a wave of wavelength

$$\lambda = h/p \qquad (1\text{-}44)$$

These waves are known as *de Broglie waves*.

Unlike a normal wave equation, Schrödinger's equation does not contain time or frequency. Equation 1-16 contains the time, and if the frequency is constant, we can write $\partial^2 \xi/\partial t^2 = -\omega^2 \xi$. Equation 1-16 then becomes

$$\frac{\partial^2 \xi}{\partial z^2} = -\frac{\omega^2}{v_\varphi{}^2}\,\xi$$

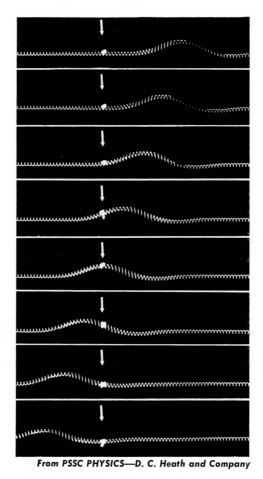

From PSSC PHYSICS—D. C. Heath and Company

PLATE I   The motion of a pulse from right to left along a spring with a ribbon at the midpoint. The ribbon moves up and down as the pulse goes by, but does not move in the direction of motion of the pulse.

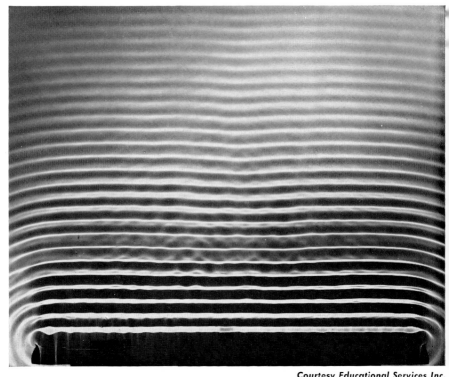

Courtesy Educational Services Inc.

PLATE II Periodic straight water waves moving across a ripple tank. The straight-wave generator is at the bottom. Curvature due to diffraction can be clearly seen.

PLATE III Reflection of periodic straight waves by a barrrier in a ripple tank. Straight waves moving upward in the photograph are reflected toward the left as they hit the barrier. (Cf. Fig. 4-1, p. 61.)

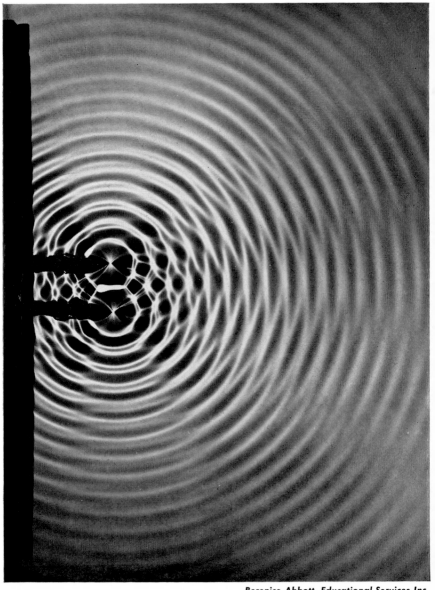

PLATE IV   Interference of water waves from two sources, illustrating the principle of Young's slits. (See pp. 62-64.)

and $\omega/v_\varphi = 2\pi/\lambda$, so that

$$\frac{\partial^2 \xi}{\partial z^2} + \frac{4\pi^2}{\lambda^2}\,\xi = 0 \qquad (1\text{-}45)$$

Like Schrödinger's equation, this does not contain time or frequency or phase velocity. For a particle in the absence of any potential field, Schrödinger's equation becomes, in one dimension,

$$\frac{\partial^2 \psi}{\partial z^2} + 4\pi^2 \cdot \frac{2Wm}{h^2} \cdot \psi = 0 \qquad (1\text{-}46)$$

and comparison of equations 1-45 and 1-46 shows that the equivalent wavelength is

$$\lambda = h\,\sqrt{\frac{1}{2Wm}}$$

Since W, which for $V = 0$ is the kinetic energy, is $p^2/2m$, we obtain $\lambda = h/p$ as above.

It is fitting that the frequency and phase velocity should not be explicit in Schrödinger's equation, for these quantities cannot be observed practically. Only wavelength can be observed, by diffraction methods. But Schrödinger's equation is still a wave equation, just as is equation 1-45; it is the wave equation for de Broglie waves.

A group velocity can also be defined; this, as we saw in § 8, is the velocity of flow of energy. In the present case, it can be equated to the velocity of the particles, which is appropriate, since the particles carry the energy.

2   *Reflection and Refraction*

§ 13. The propagation of waves in an extended medium is best thought of in terms of *Huyghens's* * *principle*. Each point on a wavefront can be thought of as a source of secondary waves, and the position of the wavefront at some future time is given as the envelope

* Christian Huyghens, 1629–1695, was a Dutch scientist famous for work on the telescope, on clocks, and on the theory of wave motion.

of the secondary waves. The construction is illustrated for the case of a plane wave in Fig. 2-1. At some instant $t = t_1$, a number of circles are drawn, centered on points in the wavefront at $t = t_1$, to represent waves radiating from these points. Theoretically, an infinite number of such circles should be drawn, and the envelope then gives the new wavefront illustrated, parallel to the first. This construction can be applied to waves of any kind.

The above example is trivial, but the value of Huyghens's principle becomes apparent when considering the effects on propagating waves of large extended discontinuities in the medium in which they are propagating. Waves are then reflected and refracted, and this forms the subject of the present chapter. When the discontinuities are small, the waves are diffracted; this topic will be treated in Chapter 4.

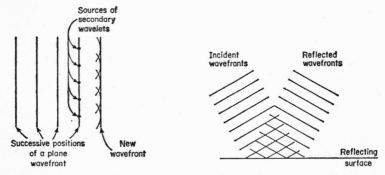

(Left) FIG. 2-1   Huyghens's construction for a plane wave. (Right) FIG. 2-2   Reflection of plane waves at a plane surface.

Huyghens's principle is essentially a mathematical method for constructing the future position of a wavefront, given its present position. As such, it belongs to the considerable battery of mathematical techniques for deducing facts about waves when other facts are given—the mathematical system which is implicit in the word "wave," and whose existence it is, in fact, that gives meaning to the word. This system has one defect: it is ambiguous; it cannot, in itself, tell us which way the wave is traveling. Equation 1-16, the wave equation, contains v_φ^2 and so is equally applicable whether v_φ

is positive or negative. Equation 1-15, which is a solution of the wave equation, represents a wave traveling one way or the other according to the sign of v_φ. To assign a sign to v_φ, one must resort to a knowledge of the physics of the situation; the mathematics is equally applicable, whatever the sign, but does not tell us how to decide on the sign. Similarly, Huyghens's principle tells us how to construct a new wavefront from a given one, *provided we know which way the wave is traveling.* This knowledge is implicit in the construction of Fig. 2-1. When using Huyghens's construction to treat reflections and refractions, it is necessary to apply a certain amount of common sense; out of several possibilities we have to choose the right ones, and these will be the ones which accord with observation.

§ 14. The simplest case of reflection is that of a plane wave striking a perfect plane barrier, i.e., a surface between two media, in one of which the wave propagates while the other is completely impenetrable to it. Examples are the reflection of sound waves at a rigid wall, the reflection of water waves at the surface of a rigid medium, and the reflection of electromagnetic waves at the surface of a perfect conductor. Of course, rigid media and perfect conductors do not really exist, but the former are approximated very closely by stone walls, and many metals—e.g., copper, silver, aluminum—are good approximations to perfect conductors.

Huyghens's construction for reflection at a perfect plane reflector is illustrated in Fig. 2-2, where the plane wavefronts of the incident and reflected waves are constructed in the manner of Fig. 2-1. The construction in the neighborhood of the reflecting surface is illustrated in Fig. 2-3. PQ is an incident wavefront, at the instant when P has just reached the reflecting surface. The end Q still has to travel to S. The arc AA', centered on P, is drawn with radius $PR = QS$. The reflected wavefront is then RS, the tangent from S to the arc AA'. BB' and CC' are drawn with equal radii, with centers S and R respectively. The common tangent of BB' and CC' is UV, a further wavefront of the reflected wave.

The triangles PQS and PRS are congruent, since PS is common, $RP = QS$, and the angles SRP and PQS are right angles. Hence $\angle QSP = \angle RPS$, i.e., the angle of incidence is equal to the angle of reflection; this is *Snell's law.*

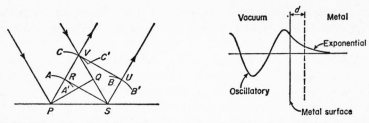

(Left) FIG. 2-3 Huyghens's construction for Fig. 2-2. **(Right) FIG. 2-4** Evanescent waves near a metallic surface.

§ 15. A line drawn perpendicular to the wavefront forms a *ray*, and it is legitimate to think in terms of rays if it is legitimate to speak of plane waves, i.e., if the wavefront extends over a large area, so that edge effects can be neglected. In principle, a plane wave must be infinite in extent, but if a beam is very wide compared with a wavelength, it may be taken as a close approximation to a plane wave. Actually, the wave will tend to spread slightly at the edges, but this effect is negligible for a sufficiently wide beam propagating over a limited distance. In optical systems set up in laboratories, or over large stretches of the earth's surface, the spreading is negligible and so may be ignored in discussing the behavior of optical instruments. Geometrical constructions can then be used to trace the paths of rays through lens and mirror systems. In other situations, however, the spreading is important; we shall return to this question in Chapter 4.

§ 16. A metal is not a perfect conductor, and so is not a perfect barrier to an electromagnetic wave. If a wave has its E vector tangential to the reflecting surface, it would have to be zero at the surface of a perfect conductor in order to avoid setting up an infinite current. The E vector is not zero, nor is it necessarily approximately zero, at a metallic surface, but has a finite value which dies away to zero very rapidly as the wave penetrates into the metal. Figure 2-4 shows a graph of the E vector of a wave near a metallic reflecting surface. Outside the metal, it is oscillatory in space, but on reaching the metal it decays exponentially. If the metal is very thick, the E vector dies away completely, and the wave is totally reflected except for a small amount of energy which is absorbed, because of the resistance of the metal. A wave whose amplitude decays rapidly in this way, with almost total reflection, is called an *evanescent wave*.

The E vector causes current to flow in the metal, and the current at a given depth is proportional to the value of the electric field. If the metal is considered to be infinitely thick, and the total current is calculated, it is found to be the same as would flow in the sheet of metal of depth d (Fig. 2-4), if in this thickness the current density were constant and equal to the value that it has in fact at the surface of the metal. The distance d is such that the field at depth d is $1/e$ of its value at the surface, e being the base of natural logarithms, 2.718. . . . It is called the *skin depth*, for a reason which will be seen later (§ 63).

It can be shown that

$$d = \sqrt{\frac{\lambda_0}{377\pi\mu\sigma}} \text{ meters} \qquad (2\text{-}1)$$

where λ_0 is the free-space wavelength in meters, μ is the relative permeability ($= 1$ for most materials), and σ is the conductivity of the metal in mhos/meter. For copper, $\sigma = 5.80\cdot10^7$ and $\mu = 1$. Hence

$$d/\lambda_0 = 3.82\cdot10^{-6}/\sqrt{\lambda_0} \qquad (2\text{-}2)$$

Thus at microwave and all lower frequencies, d is a very minute fraction of a wavelength, so that to consider the reflection as taking place at the surface of the metal does not cause appreciable error. The significance of the skin depth will be seen when we consider transmission lines and waveguides in Chapter 5.

The rate of decay of amplitude is given by $e^{-x/d}$, x being the distance into the metal. In optics, the decay is often given as $e^{-2\pi\kappa_0 x/\lambda_0}$, κ_0 being a constant called the *extinction coefficient*. Comparing these expressions, we find

$$\kappa_0 = \frac{\lambda_0}{2\pi d} = \sqrt{\frac{377\lambda_0\mu\sigma}{4\pi}}$$

At X-ray and γ-ray wavelengths, as we saw in Chapter 1, § 10, the metal can no longer be regarded as homogeneous, and the above discussion does not apply. At infrared wavelengths the skin depth becomes comparable with atomic radii—for example, at a (free-space) wavelength of 70,000 Å the skin depth for copper is given by equation 2-2 as 1 Å. We thus expect that at infrared and optical frequencies the currents induced in a metal will be affected by the atomic nature of the metal, and in fact metals give much greater losses at these frequencies than at microwave frequencies. It is therefore not strictly justifiable to relate κ_0 and d as above. This point will arise again in connection with fiber optics (§ 71).

The reflecting power, defined as the ratio of the power in the reflected wave to that in the incident wave, differs according to the plane of polarization—whether the electric vector is parallel or perpendicular to the *plane of incidence*, which is the plane containing the incident and reflected rays. It is also dependent on the angle of incidence; Fig. 2-5 shows the general form of reflecting curves for metals, the signs ⊥ and ‖ applying respectively to rays whose electric vectors are perpendicular and parallel to the plane of incidence. The reason for the minimum in the case of the parallel ray is similar to that for the zero when the reflection is from the surface of a transparent dielectric such as glass; this will be discussed in § 17. The energy not reflected is dissipated in the metal, because of its resistance to the induced currents.

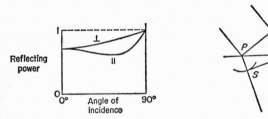

(Left) FIG. 2-5   Reflecting power of a typical metal, for waves with *E* vectors perpendicular and parallel to the plane of incidence. (Right) FIG. 2-6   Refraction at a plane surface

When light from the sun reflects from a metal surface, one component of the reflected light is much smaller than the other because of the difference in reflecting powers, and the resultant of the reflected components forms a partly polarized ray. The polarized component has its electric vector horizontal. Polaroid sunglasses contain a film of material which to a large extent stops the passage of a ray polarized one way, while allowing the other to pass through unhindered. By arranging the film to permit the passage of vertically polarized light, the horizontal component, which is the main contributor to glare, is stopped. Light reflected from water surfaces has its glare removed in a similar way. Other light, scattered from grass, trees, buildings, and other nonshiny surfaces, loses only half its intensity, so that glare is reduced far more than general lighting. This is a great improvement on cheaper forms of sunglasses, which merely reduce all light by means of dark glass; this reduces glare, but at the cost of making it less easy to see.

§ **17.** When light is incident on a surface dividing two transparent media, such as air and glass, there is both reflection and transmission, and the situation is different according as the incident ray lies in the optically less dense or more dense medium. (The optically denser medium is the one with the higher refractive index.) We consider first the case of the incident ray lying in the optically less dense medium, and take as a specific example the refraction and reflection at a glass-air interface.

Huyghens's principle can be used as in Figs. 2-2 and 2-3 to construct the wavefronts of the reflected ray; Fig. 2-6 illustrates the construction for the refracted ray. While the ray paths are given by these constructions, they give no information about the relative intensities of the reflected and refracted rays. PR is the incident wavefront, and when P reaches the surface, R has a distance RQ to travel, at velocity c (c is the velocity of light in free space; we neglect the difference between air and vacuum). During the time this takes, equal to RQ/c, a wave from P will give rise to a wavefront illustrated by the arc centered on P. The tangent QS from Q to this arc gives the new wavefront. The time taken to travel the distance PS is PS/v, where v is the velocity of light in the glass. Thus $PS/v = RQ/c$, i.e.,

$$\frac{RQ}{PS} = \frac{c}{v} \tag{2-3}$$

The quantity c/v was defined in equation 1-26 as the refractive index μ. Hence

$$\frac{RQ}{PS} = \mu = \frac{RQ/PQ}{PS/PQ} = \frac{\cos P\hat{Q}R}{\cos Q\hat{P}S} = \frac{\sin R\hat{Q}N}{\sin T\hat{Q}N'}$$

and $R\hat{Q}N = i$, the angle of incidence, while $T\hat{Q}N' = r$, the angle of refraction. Thus

$$\mu = \frac{\sin i}{\sin r} \qquad (2\text{-}4)$$

This is the way in which refractive index was originally defined.

For light polarized with the electric vector perpendicular to the plane of incidence, there are always a reflected ray and a refracted ray. For light polarized parallel to the plane of incidence, there is a value of the angle of incidence for which there is no reflected ray. This occurs at such an angle of incidence that the reflected and refracted rays are perpendicular; this value of the angle of incidence is called the *Brewster angle*. One may think of the Huyghens secondary sources in the wavefront as consisting in oscillations of electrons in the surface of the glass. These are caused to oscillate by the incident wave, and reradiate in all directions. The directions of the reflected and refracted rays are those in which the secondary wavelets all add up correctly; in other directions they add up in such a way as to give zero net amplitude. When the incident ray is polarized parallel to the plane of incidence, the electrons oscillate in this plane, perpendicular to the ray path of the refracted ray. When this is perpendicular to the direction of the reflected ray, the electrons have no component of motion perpendicular to the reflected ray, and so cannot set up an electric field vector with a component transverse to the direction of the reflected ray. Thus no reflected ray is excited. The Brewster angle is the angle whose tangent is equal to μ.

Fig. 2-7 shows the reflection curves for a typical glass surface, taking $\mu = 1.732$. There is a general similarity to the curves of Fig.

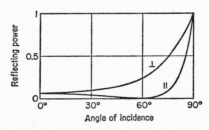

FIG. 2-7   Reflecting power of a medium with refractive index 1.732. $\perp$ and $\parallel$ denote E vector perpendicular or parallel to plane of incidence.

2-5 for the metallic case. In the metallic case, the minimum of the lower curve is related to the zero of the lower curve for the dielectric case. The reason it does not reach zero is related to the fact that in the metal the wave suffers rapid exponential decay (§ 16), while in the dielectric the refracted wave is a normal oscillatory wave, without exponential decay in the ideal, lossless case. More than this cannot be said here; the significance of this connection can only be discussed at a mathematical level beyond that of this book.

§ 18. For a ray in glass, incident on a glass-air interface, the Huyghens construction of Figs. 2-2, 2-3, and 2-6 can be used to determine the paths of the reflected and refracted rays. For the refracted ray, we may consider Fig. 2-6, with the rays reversed. We have

$$\mu = \frac{\sin R\hat{Q}N}{\sin T\hat{Q}N'}$$

and $\mu > 1$. The greatest value of $\sin R\hat{Q}N$ is 1, when the ray lies in the plane of the glass surface. This gives a maximum value of the angle $T\hat{Q}N'$, above which no refracted ray is able to emerge from the glass. At and above this value, there is *total internal reflection*—all the energy of the incident wave goes into the reflected wave. Then

$$\sin T\hat{Q}N' = 1/\mu \tag{2-5}$$

The angle of incidence θ_t, at which total internal reflection just starts, is called the *critical angle*, and is related to the Brewster angle θ_b by

$$1/\mu = \sin \theta_t = \cot \theta_b \tag{2-6}$$

Consider again Fig. 2-6, with the ray incident on the surface from within the glass, and let the angle of incidence be equal to the critical angle. Then no ray emerges from the block, but there is an evanescent wave just outside the block, with exponential decay in the direction perpendicular to the surface. As successive parts of the wavefront intersect with the surface, the wave travels along the surface. At a given point in the surface, it has a phase equal to that of the incident ray. Thus its phase differs along the surface, and in this direction it is not exponential but oscillatory. This is an example of a *surface wave*. Such waves are not at present of great interest in optics, but are of importance at radio and microwave frequencies.

For sufficiently large wavelengths, they are able to follow a curved surface—above 1,000 meters wavelength, they will follow the earth's curvature.

§ 19. For a wave normally incident on an interface between two media, there is no distinction between one polarization and the other. Let μ_1 be the refractive index of the medium in which the incident ray travels, and μ_2 that of the medium into which it is refracted. Then the *reflection coefficient* for light waves is

$$r = \frac{\mu_2 - \mu_1}{\mu_2 + \mu_1} \tag{2-7}$$

r being defined as the ratio of the square root of the power of the reflected ray to that of the incident ray. From equation 1-26, it is clear that this may also be written

$$r = \frac{v_1 - v_2}{v_1 + v_2} \tag{2-8}$$

where v_1 and v_2 are the phase velocities in the two media. For other than normal incidence, the formulas are more complicated.

If $\mu_2 < \mu_1$, r is negative; this means that the reflected wave undergoes a phase change of 180° on reflection. (This phase change also takes place if the angle of incidence is not zero.) In the case of metallic reflection, the phase change varies from 180° at normal incidence to zero at grazing incidence, for both polarizations.

§ 20. Metallic reflection is a phenomenon peculiar to electromagnetic waves; sound and water waves, for example, are not reflected in this way from any known medium. All media have similar properties, with regard to sound or elastic waves, as do dielectrics with regard to electromagnetic waves. Equation 2-8 cannot be applied as it stands, however. Every medium has a characteristic property known as the *wave impedance*—or rather, a number of wave impedances, one for each kind of wave that it supports. The reflection coefficient at normal incidence for the boundary surface between two media having wave impedances Z_1, Z_2, is

$$r = \frac{Z_1 - Z_2}{Z_1 + Z_2} \tag{2-9}$$

It happens that for light waves, with nonmagnetic materials, the refractive index is proportional to the impedance, and equations

2-7 and 2-8 follow. For sound waves, $Z = \rho v$, where ρ is the density of the medium and v is given by equation 1-20 as $\sqrt{E/\rho}$. Thus

$$r = \frac{\sqrt{E_1\rho_1} - \sqrt{E_2\rho_2}}{\sqrt{E_1\rho_1} + \sqrt{E_2\rho_2}}$$

For sound waves reflected at a rigid wall, if 1 denotes the medium outside the wall and 2 the medium of the wall, E_2 is infinite and $r = -1$, indicating total reflection with a phase change of 180°.

Actually, of course, no barrier is perfectly rigid, but this ideal can be approached rather closely. For example, the velocity of sound in brick is about ten times that in air, and the density of brick is some thousands times that of air, so that the reflection coefficient for waves in air at a brick wall is very nearly -1. The same holds true for a water-air boundary. Transmission across a water-air boundary is therefore poor, so that it is only comparatively recently, with the development of electronic devices capable of detecting sound actually in the water, that attention has come to be paid to the sounds made by fishes and other marine creatures.*

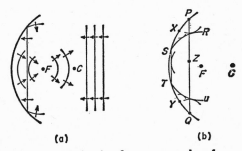

(a)   (b)

FIG. 2-8   Reflection from a curved surface.

§ 21. Huyghens's construction can be used also to determine the form of a wavefront reflected or refracted at a curved surface. As an example, Fig. 2-8(a) shows the wavefronts for an incident plane wave reflected at a concave reflecting surface, and Fig. 2-8(b) shows the construction of these wavefronts. The plane waves are reflected as converging waves, which pass through a focus F halfway between

* W. N. Kellog, "Porpoises and Sonar," University of Chicago Press, 1961.

the mirror and its center of curvature C. The direction of travel is indicated by the arrows.

Now, waves obey a *principle of reversibility*, which means that any wave system can be replaced by a system in which all the waves have their directions reversed. This fact is responsible for the ambiguity of sign of the phase velocity noted in § 13. In the example of Fig. 2-8, a point source placed at F will radiate a spherical wave. The portion radiating to the left will have wavefronts as drawn, and these will reflect in the mirror to give a plane wave moving to the right. This, incidentally, is how a searchlight or motor-car headlamp works. Thus Fig. 2-8(a) is equally correct whether the arrows are as drawn or reversed.

In Fig. 2-8(b), PQ is a wavefront whose ends have just reached the mirror at time $t = 0$. Huyghens's construction is then used to determine the position at a later time t. Circles of radius ct are drawn, centered on P and Q, c being the velocity of the wave. At some later time t', less than t, the plane wavefront intersects the mirror at points such as X and Y. The line XY (not drawn) is distant ct' from PQ, and secondary wavelets of radius $c(t - t')$ are centered on X and Y. At time t the plane wavefront has reached the position ST. The secondary wavelet centered on the point Z in PQ has radius ct, and ST is the envelope of all such circles. RS and UT are the envelopes of all circles centered on points such as X and Y.

A concave mirror is often called a converging mirror. A convex mirror causes incident plane waves to diverge after reflection, and they then appear to have passed through a focus situated behind the mirror. This is called a *virtual focus* because the waves do not actually travel through it.

Curved refracting surfaces also give focusing effects. Fig. 2-9 shows ray paths (wave normals) through various kinds of lenses for incident plane waves (parallel rays). Fig. 2-9(a) shows a biconvex lens

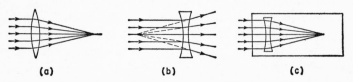

(a)   (b)   (c)

FIG. 2-9   Focusing action of lenses.

in an optically less dense medium, such as a glass lens in air, using light waves. This is a converging lens, with a real focus, through which the waves really do travel. Fig. 2-9(b) shows a concave lens surrounded by an optically less dense medium; the focus is virtual, and this is a diverging lens.

If a convex lens is surrounded by an optically denser medium, it becomes a diverging lens, and if a concave lens is surrounded by an optically denser medium, it becomes a converging lens. The latter case is illustrated in Fig. 2-9(c), where the lens consists of an air space in a large block of glass.

In Fig. 2-6 it can be seen that on entering an optically denser medium, the ray is bent towards the normal. Conversely, on entering an optically less dense medium, the ray is bent away from the normal. Examination of Figs. 2-9 shows that these principles hold good also for curved surfaces, regardless of whether the lens itself is optically denser or less dense than the surrounding medium.

§ 22. The principles discussed above apply to waves of all kinds, although our most frequent experience of them is with light waves. In this case, combinations of lenses and mirrors are used to make optical instruments. Of these, the telescope and the microscope are basic, most other instruments consisting of variations and/or combinations of these. Telescopes and microscopes consist of two principal parts, the objective, which forms a first image of the object viewed, and the eyepiece, with which the image is looked at in much the same way as objects are viewed through magnifying glasses. In a microscope, a very powerful short-focus objective is used to magnify a very near small object. In a telescope, the objective, which may be a lens or mirror, is weak, and distant objects are focused a long way from it, at its principal focus if the object is, for all practical purposes, at infinity; this is the case in astronomy.

The ideal shape for the mirror of an astronomical telescope is not spherical but paraboloidal. Parallel rays (and rays from infinity are essentially parallel) parallel to the axis are all brought to a focus at the same point, which is the focus of the paraboloidal surface. With a spherical surface, different rays focus at different points, and star images are blurred.

§ 23. Now let us consider some examples of lenses, mirrors, and "optical" instruments used with other kinds of waves. Reflection of water waves takes place at rigid surfaces, and refraction occurs when the depth changes. Water waves can be readily studied in ripple tanks*—shallow tanks of water, in which ripples are generated— and reflection at mirrors is illustrated by the insertion of rigid obstacles. Lenses may be imitated by solid blocks which reduce the depth. Reflection can also be seen when ocean waves are incident on a cliff, and sandbanks below the surface cause focusing. In these cases the image formation is not so good, because cliffs and sandbanks are not likely to be very regular in form.

When water waves in a ripple tank pass over a lens-shaped block, the crests and troughs, which form the wavefronts, can be seen to take the forms determined by the Huyghens construction. In addition, however, to the converging wave which passes through a focus on the lens axis, there will be other waves which will radiate in various directions. These are diffracted waves (see Chapter 4). Diffraction always occurs when there is a discontinuity in a medium and is most pronounced when the dimensions of the discontinuity are comparable with the wavelength. When the relevant dimension is very large, diffraction effects can often be neglected, as in designing optical lenses, which will have diameters of at least a thousand wavelengths and probably hundreds of thousands or millions. On the other hand, in a ripple tank the lens is likely to have dimensions of perhaps a few tens of wavelengths. (See Plate II.)

In the *electron microscope*, electrons are deflected and focused by "lenses" which are formed not of materials but of electric and magnetic fields. One may think of the electron as a particle being deflected by the electric and magnetic forces acting on it. Alternatively, regions of constant potential may be thought of as analogous to materials of constant refractive index. The electron waves (§ 12) are refracted as they enter regions of different potential, and so the focusing is achieved. The design of an electron microscope is complicated by the fact that the potential is not constant in a "lens" or in a part of a lens, but varies continuously from point to point. The refractive index of the lens in the eye of an animal also varies from point to point.

Microwaves are used for *radar* and *communications*, and their small

* W. Llowarch: *Ripple Tank Studies of Wave Motion*, Oxford University Press, 1961.

wavelength often makes optical techniques useful. The system of Fig. 2-8 is a common form of *aerial*, in two or three dimensions. In three dimensions the mirror, or *dish* as it is often called, is a paraboloid, and the "point source" is the end of a waveguide (Chapter 5), probably with a small horn. The horn gives virtually no wave in the desired beam direction; the approximately spherical waves radiate towards the dish, where they are reflected to give a plane wave. The two-dimensional version of this aerial consists of a portion of a parabolic cylinder bounded by two plane surfaces normal to the parabolic surface (Fig. 2-10). Such a mirror is known to radio engineers as a *cheese*. The rectangular aperture of the cheese is fed by a horn which has its principal dimension perpendicular to that of the aperture of the cheese. The horn radiates a flattish beam, spreading in the principal plane of the cheese but not in the perpendicular direction. This beam is reflected by the cheese, whose apperture is so oriented as to prevent spreading of the beam parallel to the principal plane of the cheese. Thus between them the horn and the cheese send out a comparatively narrow beam. This method of "shaping" the beam will become clearer after reading Chapter 4.

While these aerials have dimensions large compared with a wavelength, they are not so very large, and the form of the radiation they give rise to is only approximately in accordance with geometrical optics. Their behavior is complicated by diffraction effects, which will be treated in Chapter 4.

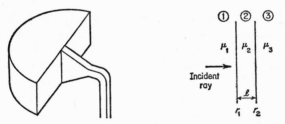

(Left) FIG. 2-10   Microwave "cheese" aerial. (Right) FIG. 2-11

These aerials can also act as receiver aerials; by the principle of reversibility, the waves are merely reversed. The dish or cheese collects radiation from a plane wave and focuses it at the mouth of the horn, whence it enters the waveguide and is conducted to the receiver. Aerials are used in this way in radar and communications systems; the same aerial may perform both functions. *Radio telescopes* work in the same way, as receiving aerials only. They are not true telescopes, since they are the radio analogues of shaving mirrors, and may also be likened to motor-car headlamps or searchlights working in reverse.

§ 24. When two reflecting surfaces are separated by a fairly small distance (by "small" is meant not considerably greater than the wavelength of the waves concerned) multiple reflections occur. The behavior of waves reflecting at the surfaces depends importantly on the distance apart of the surfaces, measured in wavelengths. Consider the two surfaces in Fig. 2-11, separating three media which are characterized by their refractive indices μ_1, μ_2, and μ_3. The reflection coefficients are (see § 19)

$$r_1 = \frac{\mu_2 - \mu_1}{\mu_2 + \mu_1}; \quad r_2 = \frac{\mu_3 - \mu_2}{\mu_3 + \mu_2} \tag{2-10}$$

and $r_1 = r_2$ if the media are so chosen that

$$\mu_3/\mu_2 = \mu_2/\mu_1 \tag{2-11}$$

i.e., μ_1, μ_2, and μ_3 are in geometrical progression.

If the reflecting surfaces are a quarter-wavelength apart, i.e., $l = \lambda/4$, the wave reflected from the surface 2 has traveled a half-wavelength more than that reflected from surface 1, and if r_1 and r_2 are equal, the two reflected waves are of equal amplitude and opposite phase. There is no overall reflection, and a wave incident on such a pair of surfaces enters medium 3 with no reflection loss. This principle is applied in the blooming of camera lenses (§ 66).

The same principle is operative when a thin film of oil spreads over the surface of a puddle of water and the rainbow colors are seen. Light of one color, for which the quarter-wave condition is satisfied, passes easily into the water and is absorbed in the ground beneath. Since the condition 2-11 will not usually be satisfied, however, the transmission into the water is not perfect and there will be some reflection. Light of another color, for which $l = \lambda/2$, will be strongly reflected because the rays reflected from the air-oil and oil-water surfaces will now be in phase. The result is to give reflections of varying color from different points on the surface: the color seen will depend on the thickness of the film at that point and on the angle of view.

This effect is exploited in the manufacture of optical interference filters,* which consist of two plates of glass between which are a number of thin films of various materials. The reflections at the various surfaces add in different phases according to the color, and it is possible in this way to design color filters to pass any desired part or parts of the visible or ultraviolet or infrared spectrum. The same principle is also exploited in waveguides and transmission lines and in interferometry (§ 41).

3   Resonance

§ 25. Consider first a *simple pendulum*. When allowed to swing freely, it performs oscillations with frequency

$$\nu_0 = \frac{1}{2\pi} \sqrt{\frac{g}{l}} \qquad (3\text{-}1)$$

where g is the acceleration due to gravity and l is the length (§ 2). Now suppose that impulses are applied to it, at an arbitrary frequency ν. After a time a dynamic steady state is set up in which the pendulum oscillates at frequency ν; the amplitude of oscillation will depend on the value of ν and will be largest when $\nu = \nu_0$ (Fig. 3-1).

When $\nu = \nu_0$, the pendulum is said to resonate; oscillations build up to a high level. At all frequencies, the steady level of oscillation is set by the balance between the rate at which energy is dissipated (through friction at the point of support and air resistance) and the rate at which energy is supplied. At resonance, energy is most readily accepted by the pendulum, because every push applied to it is in just the right sense to increase the motion, whereas at other frequencies some of the pushes are in the wrong sense and act to de-

* K. M. Greenland, "Interference Filters in Optics," Endeavour, 11, 143–148, July 1952.

crease the motion; this is why the amplitude becomes large at the resonance frequency only.

Figure 3-1 shows a typical resonance curve; the width of the curve depends on the dissipation—the greater this is, the wider and flatter the peak. The height of the ordinates expresses the amplitude of oscillation, assuming the amplitude of the excitation to be constant with frequency.

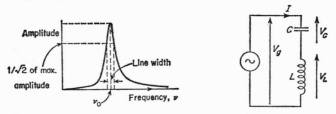

(Left) FIG. 3-1   Response curve of simple pendulum. (Right) FIG. 3-2 Series resonant circuit.

§ 26. If an electrical circuit contains both inductance and capacity, it exhibits resonance when excited by an alternating current or voltage. There are two basic kinds of resonant circuit, the series and the parallel types, illustrated in Figs. 3-2 and 3-3 respectively. In Fig. 3-2 a constant-voltage generator drives a current I through a series circuit whose impedance varies with frequency, so that I will be a function of frequency. In Fig. 3-3, a constant-current generator supplies a voltage across a parallel circuit whose impedance again varies with frequency, and this time it is the voltage across the circuit which varies. Let us consider the series circuit first.

We saw in § 9 that the current through a capacitor leads the voltage by 90°, while that through an inductor lags on the voltage by 90°. Figure 3-4 is a diagram in which these relative phase angles

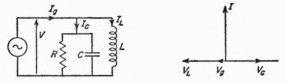

(Left) FIG. 3-3   Parallel resonant circuit. (Right) FIG. 3-4   Vector diagram of series resonant circuit.

are shown as geometrical angles; such a diagram is called a *vector diagram*, and in the present case it shows that the capacitor and coil voltages differ in phase by 180°. V_g is the net voltage; as drawn in Fig. 3-4, V_L is greater than V_c and V_g is $V_L - V_c$; the current lags on V_g. If V_c were greater than V_L, V_g would lag on I.

From equations 1-32 and 1-35 (§ 9) we have

$$V_L \sin (\omega t - \pi/2) = \omega L I \sin \omega t$$

$$V_c \sin (\omega t + \pi/2) = \frac{I}{\omega C} \sin \omega t$$

where φ has been put equal to $-\pi/2$ in equation 1-32 and to $+\pi/2$ in equation 1-35. Hence

$$V_L/V_c = -\omega^2 LC \tag{3-2}$$

The minus sign indicates that the phases differ by 180°, as is clear from Fig. 3-4.

Consideration of Fig. 3-4 shows that the circuit is reactive, i.e., the ratio of generator voltage to current is a reactance, since V_g and I are 90° out of phase. The total reactance is $V_g/I = X_s$ (s for series). Then

$$X_s = V_L/I - V_c/I = \omega L - 1/\omega C \tag{3-3}$$

Notice that at the frequency given by

$$\omega = 1/\sqrt{LC} \tag{3-4}$$

X_s is zero. Theoretically, then, I becomes infinite. In practice, there is always some resistance in the circuit, although this may be very small, and this limits the current. A graph of current against frequency then has the form of Fig. 3-1, with current as ordinate. The frequency $1/\sqrt{LC}$ is the resonance frequency, and the circuit is called a *series resonant circuit*. The resonance phenomenon that has just been described is often called *series resonance*.

Since V_L and V_c are proportional to I, these also become very large at resonance and show the behavior with frequency illustrated in Fig. 3-1. While V_g remains small, the voltage at the connection between capacitor and coil swings widely. When it is at its positive maximum, the current is zero and the capacitor is positively charged. The energy of the circuit is contained in the electric field between the capacitor plates. A quarter of a cycle later, the current is a maximum, and $V_L = V_c = 0$. The energy of the circuit is then contained in the magnetic field set up by the current in the coil. After a further quarter-cycle, the current is again zero, the voltage is a maximum in the opposite sense, and the energy is again all stored in the capacitor. Another quarter-cycle, and the voltages are zero, the current is a maximum in the opposite sense, and the energy is all stored in the coil. Thus the energy shuttles backwards and forwards between the coil and the capacitor, at twice the frequency of the current and voltage. These features are illustrated in Fig. 3-5.

This continual shuttling of the stored energy between one form and another, at twice the oscillation frequency, is a common feature of all resonant systems. In the case of a simple pendulum, for ex-

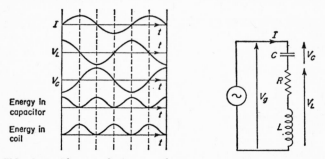

(Left) FIG. 3-5   Phase relations and energy in series resonant circuit. (Right) FIG. 3-6   Series resonant circuit with loss.

ample, the energy is all kinetic at the bottom of a swing when the velocity of the bob in either direction is greatest, and all potential at either end of a swing when the velocity, and therefore the kinetic energy, are zero. For the stretched string and the small mass suspended on an elastic cord, mentioned in § 2, the exchange is also between potential and kinetic energy.

In order to proceed further, we must consider the circuit with some resistance. Let us suppose that the resistance is all contained in the coil; the circuit is then as in Fig. 3-6. The vector diagram is given in Fig. 3-7; I and V_L are no longer at right angles, as we saw in § 9. The circuit is no longer purely reactive, but has an impedance given by

$$Z_s = \sqrt{(\omega L - 1/\omega C)^2 + R^2} \tag{3-5}$$

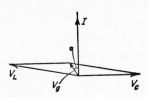 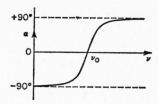

(Left) FIG. 3-7 Vector diagram of series resonant circuit with loss.
(Right) FIG. 3-8 Phase lag of current on voltage in lossy series resonant circuit.

The relation between V_g and I is shown in Fig. 3-7; V_g is obtained from V_L and V_c by completing the parallelogram and drawing the diagonal. The current lags on V_g by an angle α, with

$$\tan \alpha = \frac{\omega L - 1/\omega C}{R} \tag{3-6}$$

and the current is

$$I = \frac{V_g}{Z_s} = \frac{V_g}{\sqrt{(\omega L - 1/\omega C)^2 + R^2}} \tag{3-7}$$

If R is very small compared with the value of ωL at resonance, it is approximately true to say that Z_s is a minimum when

$$\omega^2 = \omega_0^2 = LC \tag{3-8}$$

and then $I = V_g/R$. This gives the height of the peak of a curve such as that of Fig. 3-1. When ω is either greater than or less than the resonance value, Z_s is greater than R and I is less than the value at resonance.

At resonance, α is given by equation 3-6 as zero. At lower frequencies, $\omega L < 1/\omega C$, and $\tan \alpha$ is negative; as the frequency approaches zero, $\tan \alpha$ approaches $-\infty$ and α approaches $-90°$. At higher frequencies than resonance, $\omega L > 1/\omega C$, $\tan \alpha$ is positive, and α approaches $+90°$ at high frequencies. Figure 3-8 shows α as a function of frequency; α is the phase difference between voltage and current, and the curve of Fig. 3-8 is called the *phase response* of the circuit, while the curve of Fig. 3-1, with I or Z_s or V_L as ordinate, is called the *amplitude response*. The smaller R is, the sharper is the change in α from near $-90°$ to near $+90°$, and in the limiting case of zero resistance, the change occurs discontinuously at the resonance frequency.

The power dissipated in the circuit is I^2R, for no energy is dissipated in an inductance or capacity—energy merely flows into and out of them in alternate quarter-cycles. There will be two values of frequency, one above resonance and one below, for which the power is half the peak value; then I^2 is half the resonance value, i.e., I is $1/\sqrt{2}$ of the resonance value of I. The difference between these two values of frequency is called the *bandwidth* of the circuit, i.e., the width of the band of frequencies to which the circuit is able to respond. The bandwidth and height of the resonance peak determine the sharpness of the resonance. It is convenient to define a *quality factor Q*, nowadays called simply the "Q" of the circuit:

$$Q = \omega_0/\Delta\omega \tag{3-9}$$

where $\Delta\omega$ is the bandwidth. In the particular case we are considering, it can be shown that

$$Q = \omega_0 L/R \tag{3-10}$$

In fact, this is how Q was first defined, and from this definition equation 3-9 was derived. Equation 3-10 is of very limited application, but equation 3-9 is readily applicable to any kind of resonator. Q is a very important parameter and occurs constantly in any discussion of resonance. Equations 3-9 and 3-10 are only valid if Q is fairly large, which is usually the case. For example, for ordinary AC circuits, it is likely to be between 30 and 300; for a microwave cavity it is likely to be greater than 10,000; and a typical value for an optical spectrum line is 1 million.

§ 27. Results for the parallel circuit of Fig. 3-3 are analogous to those for the series case, with voltage and current interchanged, and can be stated briefly, using the *principle of duality*. The essence of this is that series elements are replaced by parallel elements, and vice versa, inductive reactances by capacitive, and vice versa, resistances by conductances, and vice versa, and voltages by currents and vice versa. Then a formula for the impedance of a circuit is readily changed into an analogous formula for the *admittance* of the *dual* circuit. *Admittance* is a quantity having the dimensions of the reciprocal of impedance, just as in DC theory conductance is a quantity having the dimensions of the reciprocal of resistance.

The dual of the circuit of Fig. 3-6 is that of Fig. 3-3, in which L and C in series are replaced by L and C in parallel, and R in series with L is replaced by a conductance $1/R$ in parallel with C. The admittance of this circuit is then

$$Y_p = \frac{1}{Z_p} = \sqrt{(1/\omega L - \omega C)^2 + 1/R^2} \qquad (3\text{-}11)$$

in which all groups of terms are the reciprocals of the corresponding groups in equation 3-5. We now suppose I_g to be maintained constant; V is then given by

$$V = \frac{I_g}{Y_p} = I_g Z_p = \frac{I_g}{\sqrt{(1/\omega L - \omega C)^2 + 1/R^2}} \qquad (3\text{-}12)$$

and a curve of V against frequency is of the form of Fig. 3-1. This is called *voltage resonance*, because it is the voltage across the circuit which becomes large at resonance. A series circuit similarly exhibits *current resonance*.

The "Q" of the circuit of Fig. 3-3 is

$$Q = R/\omega_0 L \qquad (3\text{-}13)$$

and the vector diagram is shown in Fig. 3-9, which defines the phase angle α; α is again given as a function of frequency by Fig. 3-8.

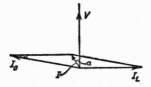

FIG. 3-9 Vector diagram of parallel resonant circuit.

§ 28. Figures 3-1 and 3-8 are very important curves in physics. If, for all values of frequency from zero to infinity, either the amplitude or the phase response is known (not necessarily the same one over the whole frequency spectrum), then the other is automatically determined, and can be evaluated by the use of special mathematical functions known as *Hilbert transforms*. This technique was rediscovered in the context of network theory by Bode, and in books on this subject the technique is often referred to as *Bode's theorem*.

Given an amplitude response of the form of Fig. 3-1, it is possible to say at once that the phase response is of the form of Fig. 3-8. That there is an interconnection is apparent on considering equations 3-6 and 3-7 in the case of electrical resonance, but it is important to realize that this is a universal result, applying to any kind of oscillating system. The more complicated the resonating system, the more complex are its amplitude and phase responses, but they are still uniquely related through Hilbert transforms.

§ 29. The above discussion of the tuned circuit applies only when the frequency is such that the dimensions of the circuit are very small compared with the wavelength of electromagnetic waves at the frequency of excitation. This assumption holds good at frequencies up to, say, 100 megacycles per second (1 megacycle per second, abbreviated to 1 Mc/s, is 10^6 c/s), corresponding to a wavelength of 3 metres. At higher frequencies, the lengths of the wires begin to become important—there is an appreciable phase difference between the ends of a wire joining two circuit elements, which is equivalent to extra capacity or inductance in the circuit. At low frequencies, the capacity and inductance of the circuit can be regarded, as we have been regarding them, as localized at points, and the connecting wires can be regarded as ideal short circuits. The values of L, C, and R for the circuit are then called *lumped constants*, and in the theory we have given, the lumped-constant approach has been used. Similarly, the discussions given in § 2 of the simple pendulum and the weight suspended on a spring are examples of the lumped-constant approach. This approach is valid as long as the string of the pendulum is very short compared with the wavelength of transverse waves on the string, or the spring is very short compared with the wavelength of longitudinal waves in the spring.

When an oscillating system is not small, it may be regarded as having distributed parameters. An electrical example is the transmission line, which for simplicity we may take in the form of two parallel wires. Between the wires there will be a small capacity, since the wires may be regarded as analogous to capacitor plates of very small area and large separation. The capacity will be proportional to length, and so instead of capacity itself we speak of capacity per unit length. There will also be an inductance per unit length associated with each wire; the reason for this will be explained in § 63.

Between the wires there will be a voltage, and along them will flow a current, the voltage and current being in the form of waves. Resonance behavior will occur when the frequency is such that the length of line is an integral number of half-wavelengths long, if it is either open-circuited or short-circuited at both ends, or when it is an odd number of quarter-wavelengths long, if it is open-circuited at one end and short-circuited at the other.

Other examples of resonance behavior in systems having distributed parameters are transverse waves on stretched strings, which we shall discuss at length in the next section; sound waves in tubes, such as organ pipes, flutes, trombones, and other musical instruments; elastic flexural waves in rods—the xylophone. The above examples apply to waves in one dimension only. Examples of resonant structures involving waves in two dimensions are stretched membranes (drum), plates (xylophone, certain kinds of microphone, diaphragm of telephone receiver, quartz plates in crystal-controlled electrical oscillators), and water waves in a tank. A natural example of water waves occurs with the tides. Sometimes these are higher than theory predicts, and the extra height is explicable as a resonance oscillation of the whole sea in a sea basin; this is a low-Q resonance, and the increased height of the tides is not great. The effect may be pictured as similar to the water sloshing about in your bath. Three-dimensional structures also give resonances—for example, electromagnetic waves in cavities, sound waves in buildings, and elastic waves in blocks of elastic material which are not thin.

§ 30. Some important features of resonance in distributed systems can be discussed in terms of the particular example of the stretched string. In § 2, it was pointed out that any element of the string performs simple harmonic motion. We now turn our attention to the string as a whole.

The first thing to notice is that the two ends are rigidly clamped, so that at these points the amplitude of the motion must be zero. This fact must be expressed mathematically and inserted into the equations governing the motion of the string. Such mathematical expressions are called *boundary conditions*, and play an important part in the study of waves in any distributed system. First we must find a general solution of the wave equation, which expresses the kinds of wave that can exist in the medium concerned—the string, in the present instance—and then we must use the boundary conditions to establish the constants of the motion—i.e., to pick out from the general solution those restricted solutions which can exist in the system actually being investigated. The details of the calculation are given here as an illustration of the procedure used for the treatment of resonance in all kinds of distributed systems.

We saw in § 4 how the solution of the wave equation could be obtained in the form

$$\xi = a \sin (\beta z - \omega t + \alpha) \tag{3-14}$$

Another solution is

$$\xi = a' \sin (\beta z + \omega t + \alpha') \tag{3-15}$$

These two equations represent waves of the same frequency, $\omega/2\pi$, and wavelength, $2\pi/\beta$, traveling in opposite directions. A more general solution is evidently

$$\xi = a \sin (\beta z - \omega t + \alpha) + a' \sin (\beta z + \omega t + \alpha') \tag{3-16}$$

and we now have to choose a, a', α, α', β, and ω in such a way that the boundary conditions are satisfied. We can write first

$$\begin{aligned}
\xi &= a\{\sin \beta z \cos (\omega t - \alpha) - \cos \beta z \sin (\omega t - \alpha)\} \\
&\quad + a'\{\sin (\omega t + \alpha') \cos \beta z + \sin \beta z \cos (\omega t + \alpha')\} \\
&= \sin \beta z\{a \cos (\omega t - \alpha) + a' \cos (\omega t + \alpha')\} \\
&\quad + \cos \beta z\{a' \sin (\omega t + \alpha') - a \sin (\omega t - \alpha)\}
\end{aligned}$$

If l is the length of the string, we require $\xi = 0$ at $z = 0$ and $z = l$, at all times. The first condition requires us to reject the solutions involving $\cos \beta z$. Hence

$$a \sin (\omega t - \alpha) = a' \sin (\omega t + \alpha')$$

for all t. This means either that $a = a'$ and $\alpha = (2n + 1)\pi + \alpha'$ or $2n\pi - \alpha'$; or that $a = -a'$ and $\alpha = (2n + 1)\pi - \alpha'$ or $2n\pi + \alpha'$, n being any integer. Taking $a = a'$ and $\alpha = (2n + 1)\pi + \alpha'$, we find

$$\xi = a \sin \beta z\{\cos (\omega t - \alpha) - \cos (\omega t + \alpha)\} \tag{3-17}$$

Taking $a = -a'$ and $\alpha = 2n\pi + \alpha'$, we obtain the same expression. The other two possibilities give $\xi \equiv 0$, and we reject them. Expanding the cosines of summed angles in equation 3-17, we obtain

$$\xi = 2a \sin \beta z \sin \omega t \sin \alpha$$

The factors a and $\sin \alpha$ are constants which cannot be separated physically, so we may as well lump them together and write

$$\xi = A \sin \beta z \sin \omega t \qquad (3\text{-}18)$$

We have not yet used the boundary condition $\xi = 0$ at $z = l$. This leads to the requirement $\beta l = n\pi$, where n is an integer. Again, the phase velocity of the waves is $\omega/\beta = \omega l/n\pi$, and this is given by equation 1-23 as $\sqrt{T/m}$. Hence

$$\omega = \frac{n\pi}{l} \sqrt{\frac{T}{m}}$$

Substituting for β and ω in equation (3-18), we obtain

$$\xi = A \sin \frac{n\pi z}{l} \sin \left(\frac{n\pi}{l} \sqrt{\frac{T}{m}} t \right) \qquad (3\text{-}19)$$

This is the equation for an oscillation in which at a point z on the string the element dz of the string performs simple harmonic motion with amplitude $A \sin (n\pi z/l)$ and frequency $(n/2l)\sqrt{T/m}$. Looking at it another way, at any instant t the wave profile exhibits a wavelength $2l/n$ and an amplitude $A \sin [(n\pi/l)(\sqrt{T/m})t]$.

This motion was obtained as the superposition of two oppositely traveling waves of equal amplitude. The composite motion consists of a wavelike profile which does not progress along the string, although the amplitude varies along the string. Such a motion is called a *standing wave*.

Figure 3-10 shows the form of the wave profile for several values

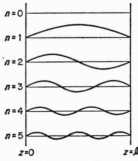

FIG. 3-10   Normal modes of a vibrating string.

of n. When $n = 0$, $\sin (n\pi z/l) \equiv 0$ and no wave exists. For $n = 1, 2, 3, \cdots$, the boundary conditions at $z = 0$ and $z = l$ are satisfied with non-zero values of A, and the amplitude is zero at a number of other points between the ends of the string. These points of zero amplitude are called the *nodes* of the vibration, and there are $n + 1$ of them (including the two end-points). The various wave profiles are called the *normal modes* (of vibration) of the system. To each mode there corresponds a characteristic frequency, and ideally the system can only be excited at one of its characteristic frequencies. In fact, however, the system will not be perfect; the ends of the string will not be clamped perfectly rigidly, it is not infinitesimally thin and weightless, as has been tacitly assumed, and there will be a certain amount of internal friction between the individual fibers of the string. This renders the line width of the resonance finite, and the amplitude response function therefore exhibits a number of peaks similar to that of Fig. 3-1 (see Fig. 3-11).

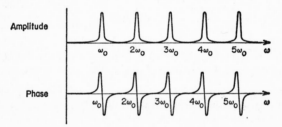

FIG. 3-11   **Frequency response of a stretched string, with resonances at multiples of the lowest resonant frequency.**

In theory, there are an infinite number of normal modes of the system, since n can take any value up to infinity. For a string of finite thickness, however, as n increases l/n will eventually become comparable with the thickness of the string, and there can no longer be the simple one-dimensional waves we have been discussing. It then becomes necessary to treat the problem as one of waves in three dimensions in a rod of appreciable thickness. There will still be an infinite number of normal modes, but they will not be the same as those calculated for the ideal model of an infinitesimally thin string. The higher thin-string modes will be increasingly distorted, becoming quite unrecognizable when l/n is of the same order of magnitude as the string thickness, although there will be a one-to-one correspondence between the thin-string modes and one set of the higher modes. In addition, there will be further higher modes due to the extra two degrees of freedom associated with the string cross section.

For a lumped-constant resonator there are a finite number of resonance frequencies—one only for the simple systems described earlier in this chapter. When several such simple systems are coupled together there will be as many resonance frequencies as there are separate resonant systems in the composite system; this may not be equal to the total number of simple systems that were combined. This contrasts with the case of a distributed-parameter system, which has an infinite number of resonance frequencies. The stretched string is a particularly simple example, in which the frequencies of the normal modes are in the ratios $1:2:3:4:\cdots$.

The equation derived above,

$$\omega = \frac{n\pi}{l}\sqrt{\frac{T}{m}} \tag{3-20}$$

was derived from a general solution of the wave equation by application of the boundary conditions. It is called the *characteristic equation* of the system, and from it the frequencies of the various normal modes can be obtained. In this case, the frequencies are given explicitly by the characteristic equation; usually it is not so simple. Not all values of frequency are possible for the system, only those which are multiples of $(1/2l)\sqrt{T/m}$. These values are called the *eigenvalues* or *characteristic values* or *proper values* of the frequency. Corresponding to each eigenvalue is a particular form of the function $\sin (n\pi z/l)$; i.e., a particular permitted frequency is chosen, and the corresponding value of n is substituted to give one particular function $\sin (n\pi z/l)$ out of the infinite number of possible functions. The function $\sin (n\pi z/l)$ is called a *wave function* of the system. Wave functions and eigenvalues occur also in quantum mechanics, and it is here that one most frequently hears the expressions, which often gives them an esoteric air. The above discussion shows that they are quite simple concepts, and there was nothing new about them when they were introduced into quantum mechanics in 1926. Most of the features we have been discussing were first systematically developed by Lord Rayleigh in his *Theory of Sound*, originally published in 1877.

Figure 3-11 also shows the phase response of the string. There is a rapid change of phase at the resonance frequencies, and the slope at resonance is negative. This is analogous to the anomalous dispersion mentioned in § 8 (see Fig. 1-11). In fact, anomalous dispersion is due to a resonance in the medium in which the wave is propagating, and so the "anomalous" behavior of the dispersion curve is explained.

§ 31. It can be shown mathematically that any shape that the string may take can be expressed as a sum of the wave functions of the normal modes, with suitable scale factors. Thus if $f(z)$ is some function of z which describes the shape in question, i.e., a function which satisfies the boundary conditions of the string, we can write

$$f(z) = a_1 \sin \frac{\pi z}{l} + a_2 \sin \frac{2\pi z}{l} + a_3 \sin \frac{3\pi z}{l} + \cdots$$

or

$$f(z) = \sum_{n=1}^{\infty} a_n \sin \frac{n\pi z}{l} \qquad (3\text{-}21)$$

where $n = 1, 2, 3$, etc. Although in this instance $f(z)$ is only expressed in the range $0 < z < l$, it is in fact a periodic function repeating at intervals of l, so that $f(z) = f(z + pl)$, where p is any integer.

The particular form of equation 3-21, involving sines, depends on the facts that at $z = 0$ and $z = l$, $f(z)$ must be zero, and that all the wave functions must be zero at these points. If we had been dealing with sound waves in a length of pipe, instead of waves on a stretched string, there would have been two principal classes of normal modes, one corresponding to an open-ended pipe, the other to a pipe closed at both ends. Taking the wave function for the displacement of the gas molecules as a function of position along the length of pipe, the boundary conditions for the closed pipe are that $f(z) = 0$ at $z = 0$ and $z = l$. This is the same problem, mathematically, as the string. For the open-ended pipe, the boundary conditions are that $df/dz = 0$ at $z = 0$ and $z = l$. Thus the displacement for a normal mode in this case is cosinusoidal, and an arbitrary displacement function can be analyzed in terms of cosine wave functions, thus

$$f(z) = a_0 + a_1 \cos \frac{\pi z}{l} + a_2 \cos \frac{2\pi z}{l} + \cdots$$

i.e.,

$$f(z) = \sum_{n=0}^{\infty} a_n \cos \frac{n\pi z}{l} \tag{3-22}$$

More generally, if the organ pipe is imperfectly stopped, the boundary conditions will be more complicated, and neither $f(z)$ nor df/dz will be zero at the ends. Then $f(z)$ can be analyzed in terms of both sine and cosine functions, thus

$$f(z) = a_0 + \sum_{n=1}^{\infty} \left\{ a_n \cos \frac{n\pi z}{l} + b_n \sin \frac{n\pi z}{l} \right\} \tag{3-23}$$

While we have presented these results in terms of vibrating strings and organ pipes, it should be clear that the results themselves are purely mathematical. The equations hold good whether $f(z)$ is merely an arbitrary curve or is the waveform of an actual wave. Let us now forget about any actual vibrating systems, and think of $f(z)$ as an arbitrary given function, periodic in z with period l. Two special cases of the boundary conditions give equations 3-21 and 3-22. More generally, the boundary conditions may be a mixture of the two special cases, and we must then use equation 3-23. Pursuing the purely mathematical idea, without considering how this may be brought about physically, these ideas may be extended to any arbitrary function, even a non-periodic function, by regarding the region $-\infty < z < +\infty$ as one period of a periodic function. Then $\pi z/l$ becomes $\pi z/\infty$, and is infinitesimally small. The sums go over to integrals, and instead of equation 3-23 we have

$$f(z) = \frac{1}{\sqrt{2\pi}} \int_{-\infty}^{\infty} g(x) \{a \cos xz + b \sin xz\} dx \tag{3-24}$$

So far we have been considering the wave function at a particular instant of time. We can equally treat the motion, as a function of time, of a particular point of the string or organ pipe or whatever resonator we may be concerned with, and obtain equations similar to 3-21, 3-22, 3-23, and 3-24, involving the time. In particular, for a nonperiodic motion we have, analogously to equation 3-24,

$$f(t) = \frac{1}{\sqrt{2\pi}} \int_{-\infty}^{\infty} g(\omega) \{\cos \omega t + j \sin \omega t\} d\omega \qquad (3\text{-}25)$$

Conversely, it can be shown that

$$g(\omega) = \frac{1}{\sqrt{2\pi}} \int_{-\infty}^{\infty} f(t) \{\cos \omega t - j \sin \omega t\} dt \qquad (3\text{-}26)$$

The expression of a periodic function in terms of sine and cosine series, or of a non-periodic function in terms of integrals, is known as *Fourier analysis*. Equations 3-25 and 3-26 are of great importance in the study of diffraction and wave filters, which will be treated in Chapters 4 and 6. The factors $1/\sqrt{2\pi}$ in these two equations are inserted so that the right-hand sides are of the same form. j is a quantity such that $j^2 = -1$, and its use is a very important feature of the mathematics of waves. The integrals of equations 3-25 and 3-26 can be handled by the methods of complex algebra, but this lies outside the scope of this book, and results will be presented qualitatively.

§ 32. The form of the response of a system capable of resonance in a number of modes depends on the form of excitation applied. If the exciting force can be Fourier-analyzed into a number of components whose frequencies are possible resonance frequencies of the system, the corresponding modes will be excited with amplitudes proportional to the Fourier coefficients of the excitation. In particular, if the exciting force consists of a single frequency equal to a resonance frequency of the system, a single mode will be excited. Conversely, if it is desired to excite the system in a particular modal pattern, which may as a special case be a single mode, the excitation must be chosen to have the appropriate Fourier components with the correct amplitudes. The statement of this principle here may seem trite, but it is a very important point and finds wide application, often unconscious. It will be mentioned again in connection with waveguides (§ 59).

§ 33. The string and organ pipe, having sinusoidal or cosinusoidal wave functions, are particularly simple forms of resonator. Others have more complicated wave functions, and the relations between the frequencies of the normal modes are more complicated. For flexural vibrations of a rod, for example, not only is the displacement zero at a clamped end, but so also is the gradient of the displacement. At a free end, there is not a true antinode, because there is nothing there physically to cause the end of the bar to be parallel to its equilibrium state. For comparison, the displacements of a bar clamped at one end and free at the other, and the particle velocities of an organ pipe closed at one end and open at the other, are shown together in Fig. 3-12, taking the third possible mode in each case. The contrast is further emphasized by comparing the resonance frequencies. For the organ pipe, with both ends either closed or open, these are the same, and are in the ratios $1:2:3:4:\cdots$. For the rod, either clamped or free at both ends, the ratios are $\sqrt{1.5056}:\sqrt{2.4997}:\sqrt{3.5}:\sqrt{4.5}:$ etc. The numbers 1.5056, 2.4997, 3.5, 4.5, etc., arise from the kinds of boundary conditions, while the square root signs arise from the fact that for flexural vibrations of elastic plates and rods the wave equation is of the fourth order. Thus instead of equation 1-15 we have, for the rod,

$$\frac{\partial^4 \xi}{\partial z^4} = -\gamma^2 \frac{\partial^2 \xi}{\partial t^2} \qquad (3\text{-}27)$$

where γ is a constant involving the elastic properties of the rod, its density, and the diameter of its cross section.

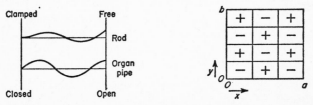

(Left) FIG. 3-12   Comparison of wave functions of elastic rod and organ pipe. (Right) FIG. 3-13   (3,4) mode of a rectangular membrane: $+$ denotes displacement upwards, $-$ denotes displacement downwards.

§ 34. The ideas we have been discussing for a one-dimensional resonator can be extended to two- and three-dimensional resonators. A membrane, clamped all round its edges, is the two-dimensional analogue of a string. The nodes are now not points but curves. In

the case of a rectangular membrane, the nodes are straight lines
parallel to the edges. If one edge is taken to define the x axis, and
a perpendicular edge to define the y axis (Fig. 3-13), the x dimension, a, is divided into p equal lengths, a/p, by $p + 1$ nodal lines, and
the y dimension, b, is divided into q equal lengths, b/q, by $q + 1$
nodal lines. The mode is the (p,q) mode; Fig. 3-13 is drawn for the
$(3,4)$ mode. The frequency of the (p,q) mode is given by the characteristic equation:

$$\nu_{pq} = \frac{1}{2} \sqrt{\frac{T}{\sigma}} \sqrt{\frac{p^2}{a^2} + \frac{q^2}{b^2}} \tag{3-28}$$

where σ is the mass per unit area of the membrane and T is its
tension, i.e., the force per unit length on a line in the membrane.
From equation 3-20, for the string, we can obtain

$$\nu_n = \frac{1}{2} \sqrt{\frac{T}{m}} \frac{n}{l} \tag{3-29}$$

The relations between the ν_{pq} for the membrane are seen to be not
so simple as those between the ν_n for the string.

For a square membrane,

$$\nu_{pq} = \nu_{qp} = \frac{1}{2} \sqrt{\frac{T}{\sigma}} \sqrt{\frac{q^2}{a^2} + \frac{p^2}{a^2}}$$

The (p,q) mode is then said to be *degenerate* with the (q,p) mode. In
this case, by rotating the membrane through 90° in its own plane,
the wave functions can be made identical. In general, however, the
wave functions of degenerate modes of resonant systems are not
identical.

As in the case of the string, any vibration of the membrane can be
expressed in terms of its normal modes by an extension of Fourier
analysis to two dimensions.

An example of a three-dimensional resonator is an electromagnetic wave in a cavity, i.e., an enclosure whose walls are all perfectly
conducting. The usual boundary conditions apply for electromagnetic waves at the surface of a perfect conductor, and can be satisfied
only for certain eigenvalues of the frequency. An atom is a resonator
for the de Broglie waves associated with electrons. Schrödinger's
equation is solved in a spherical coordinate system, and ψ is given
as a function of the coordinates r, θ, φ. The normal modes are called

states of the atom; in spectroscopy one hears of s, p, d, f, etc., states, and an s state is one having spherical symmetry, i.e., ψ is a function of r alone. In this case the boundary conditions are that at infinity there is zero probability of finding the electron, i.e., $\psi(r) \to 0$ as $r \to \infty$; and that certain relations hold between the forms of ψ just inside and just outside the value of r for which the total energy W is equal to the potential energy due to the Coulomb field of the nucleus. These conditions can be satisfied only for certain eigenvalues of W. In both these examples the calculation proceeds in a way very closely analogous to the vibrating-string calculation of § 30.

The concepts we have been discussing apply quite generally to resonators of any kind. There is a wave equation, which is solved in terms of wave functions and arbitrary constants. Relations are found between the arbitrary constants by applying the boundary conditions, and from these relations a characteristic equation is obtained which gives the allowed frequencies. These can be used to evaluate the arbitrary constants and so to get the wave functions in absolute terms. Finally, any arbitrary vibration of a resonator can be expressed in terms of its normal modes by the process of *modal analysis;* this is the same as Fourier analysis in the case of a string and is analogous to this for other resonators.

4   *Interference and Diffraction*

§ 35. There has been implicit in a large part of the preceding chapters the *principle of superposition.* When two or more electric fields exist simultaneously at the same place, the resultant field is the vector sum of the individual fields. The same is true of magnetic fields. Thus when two or more separate electromagnetic waves pass through a given point, the effective wave that may be observed at that point is obtained by summing the fields of the separate waves.

It is on this principle that Huyghens's construction depends. The radiated waves from all the secondary sources in an earlier position of the wavefront must be correctly added to find a later position of the wavefront. Secondary wavelets traveling in a direction other than that of the normal to the wavefront are found to add up to give zero (with certain reservations to be discussed in the course of this chapter). In the adding process, the principle of superposition is used.

The same principle holds good, up to a point, for all other kinds of wave. Water waves, for example, reflecting from an edge of the stretch of water (ocean waves reflecting from a cliff, perhaps), give rise to a pattern of standing waves, in which at certain points the amplitude is twice as great as in the incident or reflected waves alone, while at other points the amplitude is zero; the sea is then "choppy." If the amplitude is too great, the peaks of the superposed wave trains can be so high that the water is unable to support itself and collapses with a splash. Provided that the amplitude is not sufficiently great for this to happen, the principle of superposition holds good.

We shall only consider waves for which this principle does hold good. This means any kind of wave, as long as the amplitudes of the separate waves are such that the aggregate amplitude is not too great. For all kinds of waves, it is possible to cause the principle to break down if the wave amplitudes are too large. This happens in the case of water waves when a column of water is formed which is not stable enough to hold together for an appreciable fraction of the periodic time. Elastic waves are superposable as long as the medium is not stressed beyond the elastic limit; sound waves are superposable as long as the compression does not become so great that the gas starts to behave nonlinearly because of local heating and cooling. Electromagnetic waves would cease to be superposable if the wave fields became so large that in the devices used to detect them the accelerated charges acquired relativistic velocities.

§ 36. When two or more trains of waves of the same frequency pass through the same region of space, the amplitude seen at a given point is obtained by adding the wave displacements at that point in the correct phase relationships. This results in a standing-wave pattern, in which the waves reinforce or partially or totally cancel each other at different points. The waves are then said to *interfere.* Analogous to the above case of water waves reflecting from a cliff is the case of sound waves reflecting from the wall of a room.

Figure 4-1 illustrates such a reflection of plane waves from a plane reflecting surface. The lines parallel to *PQ* represent incident wavefronts, one wavelength apart, so that between one and the next the phase difference is 2π. Similarly, between two lines parallel to *RS* the phase difference is 2π. Along a pair of lines such as *AB* and *BC*, the phase is the same; *BC* is the reflected ray from the extension of *AB*, which has reached the reflecting surface earlier than the instant represented. At the points where the two sets of lines intersect, indicated by the heavy dots, the phase difference is a multiple of 2π, and the waves reinforce each other. A moment's thought shows that as the lines parallel to *PQ* move towards the surface and those paral-

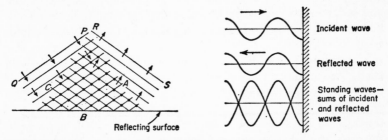

(Left) FIG. 4-1   Interference by reflection. (Right) FIG. 4-2   Standing waves.

lel to *RS* move away, the dots move to the right, parallel to the surface. Halfway between the lines traced by the dots are other lines along which the waves are always antiphase and the net displacement is always zero. These effects are readily seen on watching water waves in the sea reflecting from a sea wall. (See also Plate III.)

Figure 4-2 shows wave profiles of incident and reflected waves in the case of normal incidence. The superposed incident and reflected waves, illustrated at a particular instant of time, give *standing waves* whose envelope is illustrated. Such waves can be set up in the case of sound waves, for example, and the nodes and antinodes detected by means of a microphone. Their importance in microwave circuits will be discussed in Chapter 5.

§ 37. It should be apparent that standing waves will only be set up if the phase relation between the interfering wave trains is maintained. This means that the waves must be *coherent*, i.e., the wave must be continuous—there must be no jumps of phase, otherwise the necessary phase relationship between the incident and reflected wave trains is not preserved. Light waves from the usual sources are not coherent.* They consist of a large number of pulses of short duration, each pulse consisting of light emitted as an electron in an atom loses energy. It does this by changing from one state to another, i.e., to a different wave function and eigenvalue of energy (see § 34). Each pulse will be coherent while it lasts, but its phase relationship with other pulses will be quite random because the jumps of electrons in the various atoms from one energy level to another are quite independent. For this reason standing waves are not set up by two beams of light from separate sources; also, the very short wavelengths of light waves make optical interference effects difficult to observe, since the dimensions of the various parts of the apparatus required must be very accurately fixed. For these reasons the discovery of optical interference effects did not take place until the beginning of the nineteenth century.

§ 38. In order for interference fringes to be set up by two trains of waves, either the trains must be set up by the same source, as in the above example of reflection, or the sources must be controlled by the same oscillator. This principle was first exploited by Young at the beginning of the nineteenth century. The source consists of a slit illuminated by plane monochromatic light (i.e., light in which only a single wavelength is present, unlike white light in which are present all wavelengths in the visual range). The light is diffracted by the slit S (Fig. 4-3), i.e., it spreads out on passing through. Figure 4-3 shows plane waves incident on the slit; the light which passes through forms cylindrical wavefronts centered on the slit, in accordance with Huyghens's principle. The diffracted waves then fall on

---

* Recently devices called optical masers have been invented (see A. L. Schawlow: "Infrared and Optical Masers," *Bell Laboratories Record*, November 1960, pages 403-407), which give coherent beams of light of great intensity. It is possible to obtain two coherent beams of light from two masers which are so accurately tuned to the same frequency that the phase relationship between the beams remains constant for a considerable time. By this means, it is possible to obtain interference fringes using light beams from separate sources.

another screen in which are two slits, S_1, S_2, parallel to S and equidistant from it. Thus the waves at S_1 and S_2 have the same phase. They give rise to cylindrical wavefronts similar to that arising at S, and the light from each slit spreads over the screen. The light reaching P from S_1 will have a phase dependent on the distance d_1, which of course depends on the position of P on the screen. Similarly, the light reaching P from S_2 will have a phase dependent on d_2. The net effect at P will depend on the difference of d_1 and d_2. If this difference is an integral number of wavelengths, the waves reinforce and the screen is bright. If the difference is half a wavelength more than an integral number, the waves interfere destructively and the screen is dark. (See also Plate IV.)

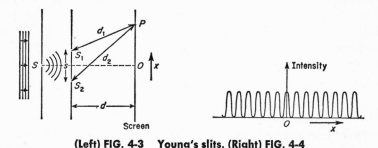

(Left) FIG. 4-3   Young's slits. (Right) FIG. 4-4

In Fig. 4-3, the dashed line SO is drawn perpendicular to the screens containing the slits and the screen on which the interfering light beams fall, and bisects S_1S_2; x is measured positively upwards from O; OP is the distance x; d is the distance SO; and s is the distance from S_1 to S_2. Then it can be shown that the intensity at P is proportional to $\cos^2(\pi xs/\lambda d)$, λ being the wavelength of the light.

A practically convenient value of d would be about a meter; λ is very small—say $5 \cdot 10^{-5}$ cm. Then xs changes by $5 \cdot 10^{-3}$ cm^2 between one maximum of the intensity and the next. In order to get an appreciable separation, s must be made small. If the fringes are to be separated by, say, half a millimeter, the slits must be only a millimeter apart.

Figure 4-4 shows the intensity distribution in the interference pattern; the bright regions are called *fringes*. There is implicit in this the assumption that the slits are of zero width. In fact, however, they must be of non-zero width if any light is to pass through them. We may consider the slits to be made up of a number of elementary lines, there being a line in one slit corresponding to each line in the other. Each pair of lines can be regarded as giving rise to a pattern of the form of Fig. 4-4, and the patterns from the various lines are displaced. These superimposed patterns are indicated in Fig. 4-5(a); they give a composite intensity pattern of the form of Fig. 4-5(b). Notice the broadened peaks and narrow troughs and the absence of complete darkness.

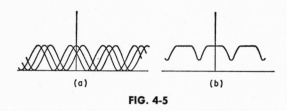

(a)   (b)

FIG. 4-5

If the widths of the slits, supposed equal, are as great as the distance between fringes, the peaks become so broadened that there are no darker regions at all, and no interference pattern is seen. The pattern becomes more visible as the slits are narrowed, but less light now gets through the slits.

Thus for fringes to be obtained, the slits must be narrow, and the source must then be bright in order to get an appreciable amount of light through the slits. The slits must be very close together, and even so the fringes are close together. If one bears in mind that prior to Young's experiment the wavelength of light was not known, it is understandable that eighteenth-century workers found it exceedingly difficult to design an experiment which successfully demonstrated the interference of light. It was Young's experiment which first permitted the determination of the wavelength of light, by measuring s, x, and d.

§ 39. A device in which beams of light, or other waves, are caused to interfere, and which is designed so that measurements can be made on the interference pattern, is called an *interferometer*. Thus the apparatus of Young's experiment constitutes an interferometer; by making measurements of the geometry of the apparatus and the distribution of the interference fringes, the wavelength of the light used can be determined. This is not a very convenient method, however, since the quantity s, being very small, is difficult to measure to any great accuracy. Two important interferometers in which this difficulty is overcome are the Michelson and the Fabry-Perot interferometers.

§ 40. *Michelson's interferometer* is illustrated schematically in Fig. 4-6(a). Light from a source S is collimated by a system of lenses*

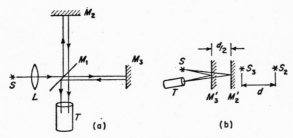

FIG. 4-6   Michelson's interferometer.

L and is partly reflected, partly transmitted, by the *half-silvered mirror* M_1. A half-silvered mirror is one with a very thin layer of silver. In § 16, it was explained that an electromagnetic wave can penetrate a short distance into a metal as an evanescent wave. If the metal is very thick compared with the skin depth, the amplitude dies away to zero and the wave is totally reflected. However, if the metal is not thick compared with the skin depth, the wave will emerge on the far side of the metal with diminished but non-zero amplitude. A transmitted wave then propagates beyond the metal, and the reflected wave is of smaller amplitude than the incident wave. By suitably adjusting the thickness of silver, a mirror can be made to split a beam into equal transmitted and reflected beams. The principle is illustrated in Fig. 4-7.

Returning to Fig. 4-6(a), the two beams leaving M_1 are reflected by the mirrors M_2 and M_3. The beam from M_2 is again partly transmitted and partly reflected at M_1, and the transmitted part enters

---

* A system of lenses which renders a beam of waves parallel is called a collimator.

the telescope T. The beam reflected from M_3 is similarly partly reflected into T.

From the point of view of the telescope, the situation is as in Fig. 4-6(b), in which M_2 is the mirror M_2, and M_3' is a virtual image of M_3. The light entering the telescope appears to come from the two virtual sources S_2 and S_3, which are the virtual images of S in M_2 and M_3'. Since S_2 and S_3 are in a coherent phase relationship, interference fringes are set up, as may be seen on considering Fig. 4-8.

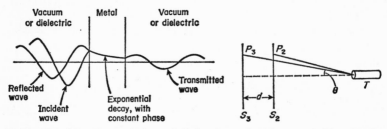

(Left) FIG. 4-7 Transmission of light through thin metal film. (Right) FIG. 4-8

The source used is an extended one. Light from a point P on the real source appears to enter the telescope from the points P_2, P_3, on the virtual sources S_2 and S_3. Brightness or darkness is seen according to the distance of P from the optic axis. The difference in distance of P_2 and P_3 from the telescope is $d/\cos \theta$, and this is to be an integral number of wavelengths for brightness or an odd number of half-wavelengths for darkness. The angle θ is the same for all points P on a circle centered on the optic axis. Thus the fringes are seen as concentric circles. One of the mirrors—M_3, say—can be moved perpendicular to its plane by a screw. As it moves, the value of $d/\cos \theta$ changes while θ remains constant. Thus the observer sees concentric bright rings growing out of or collapsing into the center of the pattern as M_3 is moved one way or the other. The appearance of one fringe corresponds to the movement of M_3 by one wavelength. Thus wavelength can be measured by counting the number of fringes which appear or disappear as M_3 is moved through a known distance.

The distance through which M_3 can be moved is limited more by mechanical than by optical considerations, as long as the light used is highly monochromatic. The sources used are usually single spectrum lines from specific atoms, but even spectrum lines spread over a small range of wavelengths, and a truly monochromatic source does not exist. The red line at 6438.5 angstroms in the spectrum of cadmium is highly monochromatic and has been used to determine the number of wavelengths in a meter by an extension of the above technique; unfortunately, space does not permit any account of the experimental details. In this way the meter was established as 1,553,163.5 wavelengths of the red cadmium line. More recently, the meter has been determined as 1,650,673.73 wavelengths of the orange-red line of the spectrum of the isotope of krypton having an atomic weight of 86, and this line was adopted in 1960 as the fundamental standard of length.

The Michelson interferometer can also be used to measure refractive indices very accurately. If a chamber of length l with transparent walls is included in one arm of the interferometer, and if it is filled with a gas of refractive index μ, its effective length is μl. Thus its effective length is $(\mu - 1)l$ greater than when it is evacuated. If the evacuated chamber is first introduced, and if the fringes appearing in the interference pattern are counted as the pressure of the gas is allowed to build up slowly, the change of effective length is $n\lambda$, where n is the number of fringes counted and λ is the wavelength. Then $n\lambda = (\mu - 1)l$, from which μ can be obtained. This is a very accurate determination, for n and l can be measured very accurately, and λ can be determined accurately as described above.

§ **41.** The principle of the *Fabry-Perot interferometer* is illustrated in Fig. 4-9. Light from a point P_1 on a source screen S_1 is collimated by the lens L_1, passes through the two reflecting surfaces R_1, R_2, and is brought to a focus at the point P_2 on the screen S_2 by the converging lens L_2. Similarly, all points on the circle C_1, whose center lies on the optic axis of the system, emit light which is brought to a focus on the circle C_2, whose center also lies on the optic axis. Multiple reflections occur at the surfaces R_1, R_2, and we shall now calculate the overall transmission and reflection.

For this purpose, consider Fig. 4-10, where the two surfaces R_1, R_2, have equal reflection coefficients r and transmission coefficients t.

In practice, the medium between R_1 and R_2 will probably be air or some gas which is being investigated, and the surfaces themselves will consist of thin films of silver on glass blocks. Reflections taking place of rays incident on R_1 and R_2 from the space between them

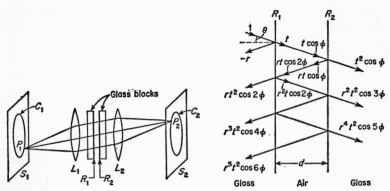

(Left) FIG. 4-9   **Fabry-Perot interferometer.** (Right) FIG. 4-10   **Multiple reflections.**

will do so with positive reflection coefficients. Some part of the incident ray, however, which is traveling in the glass, is reflected with change of phase, and so there is a negative reflection coefficient for this reflection (see § 19).

If the incident ray has amplitude 1, the first reflected ray will have amplitude $-r$ and the transmitted wave will have amplitude t. Since power is proportional to amplitude squared, we must have

$$r^2 + t^2 = 1 \qquad (4\text{-}1)$$

This expresses the fact that the sum of the reflected and transmitted powers is equal to the incident power, which is the boundary condition that must be satisfied at any surface if there is no dissipation of energy in the surface.

The incident ray is inclined at the angle θ to the normal, where θ is half the angle subtended by both circles C_1, C_2, at the point of intersection of the optic axis of the system with the plane lying halfway between R_1 and R_2.* At R_1, the incident beam is partly reflected,

* The effect of the refractive index of the glass blocks on which R_1 and R_2 are mounted has been ignored here; it does not affect the principle of the instrument.

with amplitude $-r$, and partly transmitted, with amplitude t. The transmitted wave suffers a phase change $\varphi = 2\pi d/\lambda \cos \theta$ on traversing the space from R_1 to R_2, which accounts for the factor $\cos \varphi$. At R_2, it is again partly transmitted, which introduces a further factor t, and partly reflected, with amplitude rt. Subsequent reflections and transmissions introduce further factors of r, t, and $\cos n\varphi$, to give the emergent rays indicated in the figure, n being the number of traverses from R_1 to R_2 or R_2 to R_1 that the ray has made. The net reflected ray is thus

$$R = -r + rt^2 \{\cos 2\varphi + r^2 \cos 4\varphi + r^4 \cos 6\varphi + \cdots\} \quad (4\text{-}2)$$

and the net transmitted ray is

$$T = t^2 \{\cos \varphi + r^2 \cos 3\varphi + r^4 \cos 5\varphi + \cdots\} \quad (4\text{-}3)$$

If λ is such that $d/\cos \theta$ is a half-wavelength, then φ is 180°, and $\cos \varphi = \cos 3\varphi = \cos 5\varphi = \cdots = -1$, while $\cos 2\varphi = \cos 4\varphi = \cos 6\varphi = \cdots = +1$. Hence at this wavelength, equation 4-2 becomes

$$R = -r + rt^2 \{1 + r^2 + r^4 + r^6 + \cdots\}$$

The expression in the bracket is a geometrical progression, and its sum is $1/(1 - r^2)$. Hence

$$R = -r + \frac{rt^2}{1 - r^2}$$

But $t^2 = 1 - r^2$. Thus $R = -r + rt^2/t^2 = 0$. At this wavelength, then, there is no reflected beam, and all the light is transmitted. We expect, then, that $|T| = 1$, which is the case, for equation 4-3 becomes

$$T = -t^2 \{1 + r^2 + r^4 + r^6 + \cdots\} = \frac{-t^2}{1 - r^2} = -1$$

Therefore $|T|$, which is the magnitude of T regardless of its sign, is indeed unity.

When λ is not equal to $2d/\cos \theta$, it can be shown that the sum in the bracket in equation 4-3 is

$$\frac{\cos \varphi (1 - r^2)}{1 - 2r^2 \cos 2\varphi + r^4}$$

so that

$$T = \frac{t^2 \cos \varphi (1 - r^2)}{1 - 2r^2 \cos 2\varphi + r^4}$$

Now suppose that λ is near to $2d/\cos\theta$, so that φ is near to π. Write $\varphi = \pi + \alpha$. Then

$$\cos\varphi = -\cos\alpha \fallingdotseq -(1 - \alpha^2/2)\bigg\rbrace \text{ for sufficiently}$$
$$\cos 2\varphi = +\cos 2\alpha \fallingdotseq (1 - 2\alpha^2) \quad \text{small values of } \alpha$$

and

$$T = -\frac{t^2(1 - r^2)(1 - \alpha^2/2)}{1 - 2r^2(1 - 2\alpha^2) + r^4} = -\frac{t^2(1 - r^2)(1 - \alpha^2/2)}{(1 - r^2)^2 + 4\alpha^2 r^2}$$

For small α, we can neglect the term $\alpha^2/2$ in the numerator in comparison with 1. Hence

$$T = \frac{-t^2(1 - r^2)}{(1 - r^2)^2 + 4\alpha^2 r^2}$$

At $\lambda = 2d/\cos\theta$, α is zero and this reduces to -1 as before. When α is not zero, T is not changed much if $4\alpha^2 r^2 \ll (1 - r^2)^2$, which will be the case unless r^2 is close to 1. But if r is close to 1, it is possible for $4\alpha^2 r^2$ to become greater than $(1 - r^2)^2$ while α is still small. The value of T then falls sharply.

Thus by making the surfaces R_1 and R_2 highly reflecting, light can only get through if it satisfies the condition $\lambda = 2d/\cos\theta$ to a high degree of precision, or, more generally, $n\lambda = 2d/\cos\theta$, where n is an odd integer. For a given value of λ, there will be a number of values of $\cos\theta$ for which this holds, with a corresponding set of concentric circles of brightness on the screen S_2. If we write ρ for the distance of a point on S_2 from the point where the optic axis of the system intersects S_2, ρ will be proportional to $\sin\theta$. A plot of the intensity of illumination of S against ρ appears as in Fig. 4-11.

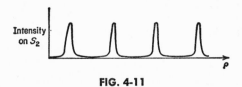

FIG. 4-11

§ 42. The similarity of form of Fig. 4-11 to Fig. 3-11 is immediately apparent. Figure 3-11 illustrates the resonances, at a number of regularly spaced frequencies, of a stretched string. The similar form of Fig. 4-11 strongly suggests that similar resonances are taking place somewhere, although the ordinates are the intensity of light falling on a screen and the abscissae are not frequencies but a distance, ρ, which is related to the wavelength of the light by

$$\frac{\lambda^2 n^2}{4d^2} = 1 + \rho^2/l^2 \tag{4-4}$$

For constant λ, there will be peaks in the curve of Fig. 4-11 for the values of ρ which satisfy this equation, one peak for each value of the odd integer n. If n is held constant and λ varied, and the amplitude on the screen S_2, at a given value of the radius ρ, is plotted against $1/\lambda$, which is equivalent to plotting against frequency, the curve obtained is similar to that of Fig. 4-11, with peaks at those values of the frequency at which the condition given by equation 4-3 is satisfied.

This behavior of the Fabry-Perot interferometer is analogous to that of a high-Q cavity in a waveguide, or of a resonant circuit between two transmission lines. The slabs of glass are analogous to lengths of waveguide, and the space between the reflecting surfaces is analogous to the interior of the cavity. Resonance takes place in the cavity when the frequency is such that the boundary conditions are satisfied. In the Fabry-Perot interferometer, there is resonance when the angle θ is such that, for the frequency actually obtaining, the boundary conditions on the surfaces R_1 and R_2 are satisfied.

Except in the resonance condition, energy cannot enter the cavity or space between the reflectors. In the resonance condition, there is a high stored energy in the resonator in both cases.

§ 43. Interferometers are also used at microwave frequencies. The standing-wave meter described in Chapter 5 is an interferometer, and can be used, in principle, to measure wavelength, although it is not so accurate as a cavity wavemeter. At higher frequencies, when the wavelength becomes less than about a centimeter, conventional cavity wavemeters become less accurate and convenient to use, as we shall see in § 67. For measurements at these frequencies, interferometric methods are used; microwave versions of the Michelson and Fabry-Perot interferometers are illustrated in Figs. 4-12 and 4-13 respectively.

§ 44. In the *microwave Michelson interferometer*, the half-silvered mirror is replaced by a beam splitter, one form of which is illus-

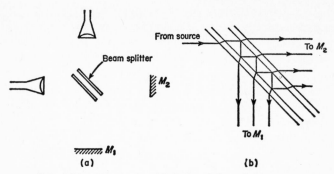

FIG. 4-12   Microwave Michelson's interferometer.

trated. This consists of two dielectric slabs, a quarter-wavelength thick, separated by an air space. The slabs act as quarter-wave transformers (§ 66), so that the energy incident on the device enters the air-space between the slabs without loss by reflection. The energy which enters this region suffers multiple reflections, and is partly transmitted, partly reflected, the relative amounts transmitted and reflected depending on the separation of the slabs. If the separation is a quarter-wavelength, the transmitted waves will add up while the reflected waves will interfere destructively, and all the incident energy will be transmitted. If the separation is a half-wavelength, all the energy will be reflected. By suitably adjusting the spacing, the energy can be made to divide equally between the reflected and transmitted waves.

Figure 4-12(b) shows the reflection process in more detail; for simplicity the multiple reflections in the dielectric slabs are ignored. Notice that in the air space between the slabs, the rays travel at 45° to the normals to the slabs, and this results in reflected and transmitted rays at 90° to each other. One travels to the mirror M_1, the other to M_2, as in the optical instrument. M_1 and M_2 are blocks of metal whose front surfaces are plated with copper or silver to render them as highly reflecting as possible, and one of them is movable.

The source consists of a horn connected via waveguides to a microwave oscillator. In the mouth of the horn is a shaped piece of dielectric to give a plane emergent wavefront. The telescope of the optical instrument is replaced by a similar horn which receives the incoming plane wave and changes its form to that of a waveguide mode. The wave is then guided into a microwave receiver. The output of the receiver is measured as the movable mirror is moved, and the maxima and minima noted. By counting a number of these, and measuring the distance moved by the mirror, wavelengths of the order of millimeters can be measured.

Since it is wavelength that is being measured, the thickness of the slabs in the beam splitter, which we have said is to be a quarter-wavelength, cannot be determined accurately. In practice, however, the slabs need only be approximately a quarter-wavelength thick; it will still work as a beam splitter even if the conditions are not ideal, and the adjustment is by trial and error. The statement that the slabs are to be a quarter-wavelength thick requires some qualification. It is not the thickness measured perpendicular to their faces that is to be a quarter-wavelength, but the distance between the faces that the beam actually travels, as indicated in Fig. 4-12(b).

§ 45. The *microwave Fabry-Perot interferometer* again uses horns, with shaped dielectrics to give a parallel beam, as source and detector. Each reflector consists of a large number of slabs of dielectric, all a quarter-wavelength thick and all separated by a quarter-wavelength, as indicated in Fig. 4-13. The effect of the multiple reflec-

FIG. 4-13

tions that occur is to give a reflection coefficient very close to unity, which, as we saw in § 39, is necessary for the production of sharp fringes.

The separation between the reflectors is something between 100 and 200 wavelengths. By moving one of the reflectors through a known distance and counting the number of maxima and minima of the detector, the wavelength is obtained.

§ 46. The phenomena of diffraction are implicit in Huyghens's theory; in fact, the Huyghens construction provides a method of computing diffraction effects. Interference phenomena are produced by the superposition of beams of light which come from a single source by different paths. One might almost say the same thing about diffraction. This occurs when some obstacle blots out part a wavefront; the diffraction effects which are observed are produced by the superposition of the secondary Huyghens wavelets radiating from all points in that part of the wavefront which is not blocked by the obstacle.

The essential feature of interference is that the part of the wavefront which is not blotted out consists of two or more regions which are of small extent in at least one dimension; one may think, for example, of Young's slits. Otherwise, it is a question of diffraction, and we either have large extents of the wavefront exposed, or a single small aperture. Thus each of the slits in Young's experiment produces its own diffraction pattern, and what is actually observed is a composite diffraction and interference pattern. More about this will be said below.

§ 47. Let us consider first the diffraction of a plane light wave by a circular aperture in a screen. Such an aperture is the circular hole C in the screen S_1 of Fig. 4-14. Light is incident on this from the left,

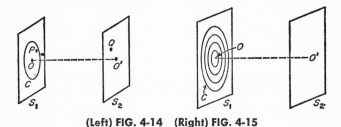

(Left) FIG. 4-14   (Right) FIG. 4-15

and that light which is incident on the interior of the circle C is able to pass on to illuminate the screen S_2. The illumination at a point such as Q is found by considering the light from a small area at such a point as P. This spreads out in all directions, and some of it reaches Q, with a certain reduction in amplitude due to the spreading out, and with a phase change depending on the time taken to traverse the distance PQ. By integrating over the interior of the circle C, the net light intensity at Q is found. The process is repeated for all points in S_2, and so the diffraction pattern is found. It consists of a series of concentric rings, alternately bright and dark.

The spot at the center, O', may be either bright or dark, according to the radius of the circle C and the distance OO' between the screens. This can be seen by imagining the circle C to be divided into a number of concentric annular zones (called *Fresnel's half-period zones*), as in Fig. 4-15. The radii are chosen so that the distance from O' to one circular boundary between zones is half a wavelength greater than the distance from O' to the next boundary. Thus the light from one zone arrives at O' in antiphase to the light from the next zone. The net intensity at O' depends on the number of zones in C; if this number is even, there are as many zones giving light in one phase as in the other, and the net intensity is approximately zero. The central spot is thus dark. If the number of zones is odd, there will be one zone whose light is not canceled, and the central spot will be bright.

The circular aperture may be regarded as having been formed by taking all the Fresnel zones, extending to infinity, and blotting out all but a limited number at the center. Conversely, a circular obstacle may be regarded as having been formed by blotting out a limited number of zones at the center, leaving all the remainder, out to infinity, to make their contributions to the intensity at O'.

The effect at O' can be understood from the vector diagram of Fig. 4-16. The vector R_0R_1 is the amplitude at O' due to the first zone. R_1R_2 is the amplitude due to the second zone; R_2R_3 is that due to the third zone, and so on. The lengths of these vectors are not quite equal because of the increased distance of the zones from O' as the radius increases. If the first n zones are present in C, the net amplitude at O' is the horizontal distance from R_0 to R_n. If n is not large, this distance may be approximately the length of the vector for a single zone, or approximately zero, giving a bright or dark

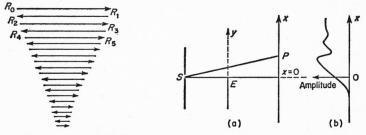

(Left) FIG. 4-16   (Right) FIG. 4-17   Diffraction at a straight edge.

central spot in the pattern of rings on S_2. If n is large, the net amplitude at O' is half that due to the first zone. In the case of a circular obstacle, the first n zones are missing, and the net amplitude at O' is given by the horizontal distance between R_n and R_∞; this is always half the nth vector, and the central spot is always bright. Thus the circular obstacle is not the dual of the circular aperture, and the pattern of light and dark rings formed by one does not give the pattern for the other merely on interchanging brightness and darkness.

§ **48.** Another important example of diffraction is that occurring at a straight edge. Consider a narrow slit S parallel to the edge E, both edge and slit being parallel to a screen X which has its plane normal to the perpendicular from a point on S to E. This is shown in section in Fig. 4-17(a). The Fresnel half-period zones are now strips parallel to the edge. On looking from P towards S, a number of these zones are seen, some above the line SP, some below, but none below E. When P is at $x = 0$, only the zones above the line SP contribute to the illumination at P. As P moves up the screen, the amplitude can be calculated for each value of x by summing the contributions from the various half-period zones. The resultant amplitude is shown in Fig. 4-17(b).

The curve shown in Fig. 4-17(b) is remarkably similar to the first part of that shown in Fig. 6-9. In fact, it is essentially the same curve; the only difference is in the units of the axes. In Fig. 6-9, the abscissae are times and the ordinates currents or voltages. In Fig. 4-17(b), the abscissae are distances and the ordinates are amplitudes of light waves. But the mathematical functions are the same.

In § 31 we introduced the subject of Fourier analysis, and we saw that even a non-periodic function can be analyzed by means of Fourier integrals. If we plot against y (Fig. 4-17(a)) the amplitude of illumination, we get the function of Fig. 4-18, which is zero for

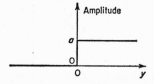

FIG. 4-18   Step function.

$y < 0$ and a for $y > 0$. Such a function is called a *step function*. Figure 4-17(b) is the *Fourier transform* of this step function. In Chapter 6 we shall consider Fourier transforms further. In the present case, with a plane wave incident on the obstacle, the Fourier transform amounts to a Fourier analysis of the amplitude function of Fig. 4-18.

§ 49. A slit, uniformly illuminated by a plane wave, can also give rise to a diffraction pattern. Figure 4-19(a) shows a slit S_1, illumi-

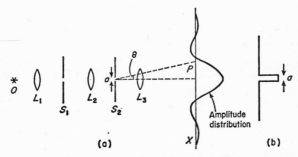

FIG. 4-19   Diffraction by a slit.

nated by a source O, at the focus of a lens L_2. Thus parallel light from S_1 passes through S_2, and is focused by the lens L_3 onto the screen X. The amplitude of illumination of the screen is as indicated.

On the opposite side of the slit S_2 to S_1, the amplitude of illumination is everywhere zero, except in the slit, where it is constant. This distribution is shown in Fig. 4-19(b); it is the spatial counterpart of the square pulse to be discussed in § 77.

The amplitude distribution on the screen X is proportional to $\sin \beta/\beta$, where $\beta = (\pi a/\lambda) \sin \theta$, λ being the wavelength, a the width of the slit, and θ the angle between the straight-through direction and the line from S_2 to the point in question on the screen X, as shown in Fig. 4-19(a). This function has zeros at values of θ such that $(a/\lambda) \sin \theta$ is an integer. Thus the greater a/λ, the smaller θ at the zeros; i.e., the wider the slit (in relation to wavelength), the narrower the diffraction pattern. In fact, if the slit S_2 is very wide, the diffraction pattern degenerates to an image of the slit S_1, while if S_2 is very narrow, the central bright region becomes very wide.

Analogously to the straight edge, the slit gives a diffraction pattern whose amplitude function is the Fourier transform of the "square-pulse" amplitude distribution of Fig. 4-19(b).

§ 50. The controversy about the particle or wave nature of light lasted for hundreds of years, and was not resolved in favor of the wave theory until the early nineteenth century, with the experiments of Young, Fresnel, and Fraunhofer. By means of carefully designed optical systems, they demonstrated interference and diffraction effects. However, no refined apparatus is required to observe diffraction effects. Diffraction by a slit can be observed with no more elaborate apparatus than the bare hands, and diffraction by a straight edge can be observed with the aid of any convenient straight edge—the edge of this book will do very well—and another distant straight edge, such as the corner of a building or a telegraph pole, with the sky behind it.

To observe diffraction by a slit, hold up one hand an inch or two in front of the face, with the fingers touching. Between the fingers there will be a number of narrow gaps. On looking through one of these at the sky or a blank, well-lit wall, with the eye focused on infinity, a number of light and dark bands can be seen.

For diffraction by a straight edge, a distant straight edge, such as the corner of a building, serves as source. A good contrast is needed, so that the building should stand out against the sky. Hold a book or ruler in the hand, with its edge parallel to the distant edge. Look at the distant edge, and move the book slowly so as to occult it. When the distant edge, book edge, and eye are approximately in line, the distant edge can be seen to split into a number of images, corresponding to the various maxima of the diffracted light. A variant is to use the edge of a window-frame as the nearer straight edge, and then move the head.

§ 51. The diffraction of sound and water waves are phenomena which we are familiar with in everyday life. When water waves from the sea are incident on a harbor wall which has a gap to provide access to the harbor, the situation is analogous to the diffraction of light by a slit. Inside the harbor, the water waves spread according to the $(\sin \beta)/\beta$ law of § 49. In this case, a is the width of the harbor gateway. The greater a/λ, the less spreading there is. Thus short waves tend to go straight through the gateway and across the harbor, while long waves bend round to fill up the whole harbor. Long ocean waves are diffracted by headlands and spread to fill bays. The behavior of water waves around coasts determines the form of the coastline.*

Sounds, as is well known, are easily heard round corners. This is because of their much longer wavelength than light waves, so that they are diffracted through large angles.

§ 52. Some microwave aerials were mentioned in § 23. With these aerials, geometrical optical techniques are used, as described in Chapter 2. However, diffraction always occurs when waves pass through a finite aperture, and when the aperture is relatively small compared with a wavelength, the diffraction is important. This is always the case with the microwave aerials used in communications and radar.

Let us consider, for example, the radiation from a horn which is supplied at its small end by means of a rectangular waveguide (Fig. 4-20), and which opens out in the plane of the broad side of the waveguide only, i.e., the height remains constant. The aperture now

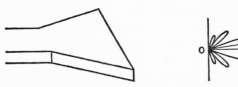

(Left) FIG. 4-20   Electromagnetic horn. (Right) FIG. 4-21   Radiation pattern (polar diagram) of horn.

approximates to a slit, and limits spreading in the horizontal plane (as drawn). Figure 4-21 shows a plot of the radiation pattern in the horizontal plane. A line from the origin, at an angle θ to the guide axis, intersects the curve at P. The length OP is proportional to the amplitude of the radiation in the direction θ, on a logarithmic scale. The radiation pattern consists of a main lobe and a number of side lobes. This is merely another way of plotting the same sort of information as is given in Fig. 4-19(a), and the plot is called a *polar*

* See, e.g., Chapter 9 of *The Face of the Earth* by G. H. Dury (Pelican Books, 1959).

diagram. If the illumination of the aperture were uniform in the case of the microwave horn, there would be an exact equivalence. The form of the radiation pattern is modified, however, by the fact that the illumination varies across the aperture, being roughly the same as in Fig. 5-8(a), with an increased *x* dimension. Both the illumination intensity and the function which describes the aperture must be taken together in forming the Fourier transform in order to obtain the radiation pattern. This is analogous to the method of obtaining the response function of an electrical network, which depends on the input waveform and the transfer function of the network. We shall consider this in §§ 76 and 77. The analogy is discussed further in § 78.

It is important with radar aerials to obtain narrow main lobes, with the side lobes as small as possible. Otherwise, strong reflections of power in the side lobes might be mistaken for weak reflections of power in the main lobe. This could have disastrous consequences, for example when guiding aircraft to land in a fog. Figure 2-10 shows a common type of aerial; the horn, being wide in the vertical plane, causes the beam to be narrow in the vertical plane, while the cheese, having an aperture wide in the horizontal plane, limits the horizontal width of the beam.

§ 53. When interference patterns are set up, they are modified by the diffraction patterns of the slits. Figure 4-4 shows the interference pattern from a pair of slits as having the maxima all of the same height. Because of diffraction, however, the maxima will actually have heights proportional to the height of the diffraction curve. Thus the interference pattern will be as in Fig. 4-22.

§ 54. Fourier transform theory can also be applied to diffraction by gratings. A diffraction grating is a structure having a spatially

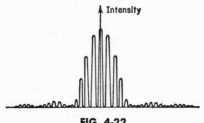

FIG. 4-22

periodic variation of transmitting power, and this variation can be Fourier-analyzed into a number of sinusoidal components with certain amplitude coefficients. If the variation of transmitting power is sinusoidal, all the light of a plane wave incident on the grating goes into the two first-order spectra. If the nth harmonic is present in the Fourier spectrum of the grating, there will be an nth-order diffracted wave, with amplitude proportional to the nth Fourier coefficient.

If a microscope is used to examine a diffraction grating which is illuminated by a plane wave, what is seen depends on how many of the diffracted waves enter the microscope. If the objective of the microscope is sufficiently wide to admit all the orders of diffracted waves, the grating will be seen as it really is. If only the first n orders are admitted, the grating will appear to be identical with a grating whose Fourier spectrum contains only these first n orders, with the same amplitude coefficients. Because of the absence of the $(n + 1)$th, $(n + 2)$th, etc., orders, the grating will be recognizable, but will not appear as it really is. If only the zeroth-order diffracted wave is able to enter the microscope, there is no difference between this light and that which would enter the microscope if there were no grating present at all. Thus no grating is seen—it looks just as if there is nothing there.

This point was first realized by Abbé, who pointed out that in order for an object to be seen at all under the microscope, at least two orders of diffracted light must be able to enter the objective. In the early days of microscopy, bacteria were described with all sorts of whiskers and wrinkles, and different workers saw different features in the same species. Abbé showed that the whiskers, if they really existed, could not possibly have been seen with the microscopes then existing because the diffracted waves from the whisker would diverge at too great an angle for more than the zeroth-order wave to enter the microscope.

A microscope can only observe objects which are above a certain size; the resolving power of a microscope is a measure of how small an object can be seen. The angular separation of the zeroth- and first-order diffracted waves is greater, the smaller the object, and resolving power can therefore be regarded as a manifestation of the principle of Fourier analysis.

5   *Guided Waves*

§ 55. When there is a discontinuity in the medium in which a wave is propagating, there is a tendency for the wave to follow the surface of discontinuity. We have already seen one example of this in § 18, when a beam of light in a glass block is incident on the surface at the critical angle, giving rise to a surface wave which propagates along the surface of the block, outside it, parallel to the plane of incidence. A surface wave is only a special case of a guided wave, but some people like to preserve in their minds an artificial distinction between surface waves, when the dimensions of the guiding structure are large compared with a wavelength, and guided waves when the dimensions of the guiding structure, in the plane perpendicular to the direction of propagation, are comparable with a wavelength.

The guided waves that have been most extensively studied are electromagnetic waves in the microwave range of frequencies, traveling in metal tubes and other structures. These are extensively used in microwave transmitters and receivers, which play an important part in our lives, for microwaves are used in radar systems for navigational and look-out purposes at sea and in the air, and for communication across jungles and deserts and mountainous country where the maintenance of wire communication systems would be uneconomic. But men were using guided waves long before the advent of radar—before even electromagnetic waves were discovered—from before the dawn of history. Guided waves were probably exploited by anthropoid species long before *Homo sapiens* came along, although it was only at the end of the nineteenth century that men formulated the concept of a guided wave. For many musical instruments make use of guided sound waves; organ pipes, and the tubes of flutes, clarinets, trumpets, and the like—all these are acoustic waveguides, and so were the pipes of Pan.

Mechanical waveguides are also much in use nowadays—elastic

82

waves traveling along rods and in discs. We shall say something of these, and acoustic waveguides, in § 69.

A natural waveguide is found in the atmosphere when there is a temperature inversion. Usually, the temperature decreases with increasing height, but it can sometimes happen that it decreases from the ground to a minimum at a height of some miles, after which it increases. At the minimum temperature, the density is greatest, and for sound waves the velocity, given by equation 1-19, is a minimum. Under these conditions, the sound wave tends to be guided by the sheet of air of maximum density. Thus the sound spreads two-dimensionally instead of three-dimensionally, and the intensity falls off inversely with distance from the source instead of inversely with the square of distance. If the guiding duct is near the ground at the source, and also at some distant point, the sound is heard at that distant point more strongly than under normal conditions, while at intermediate distances the duct will be high above the earth's surface and the sound will not be heard. This accounts for the reports of battles heard at abnormally great distances, while people nearer to the battlefield have heard nothing.

The same effect takes place with radio waves, which also have a minimum velocity where the air has a maximum density. In the same way, signals are sometimes heard at abnormally great distances, while they have not been received at shorter distances, at such places and times of day that these effects cannot be attributed to reflection by the ionosphere. It has occasionally happened that distant scenes have been seen clearly in the sky; this can be attributed to a similar effect occurring at optical frequencies.

§ 56. Perhaps the simplest waveguide to discuss first is the *parallel-plate guide*, which consists of two parallel metal plates separated by air or a dielectric material. Electromagnetic waves travel in the space between the plates. Figure 5-1 shows a cross section of such a guide. For convenience, the metal plates may be regarded as perfect conductors, i.e., as conductors with infinite conductivity. Metals are such good conductors that the difference between a metal and a perfect conductor can be ignored for many purposes.

The simplest wave that can be supported by this waveguide is part of a *plane wave*. In a plane wave, the lines of electric force are straight and parallel, extending to infinity, and are directed perpendicular to the direction of propagation, i.e., they lie in the transverse plane. The lines of magnetic force also lie in the transverse

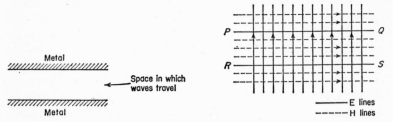

(Left) FIG. 5-1   (Right) FIG. 5-2   Plane electromagnetic wave.

plane, at right angles to the electric lines. This field configuration is illustrated in Fig. 5-2. The lines PQ and RS represent surfaces extending in the direction of propagation, i.e., perpendicular to the paper. They are drawn parallel to the magnetic lines and perpendicular to the electric lines. Now, an electric line of force must be perpendicular to the surface of a perfect conductor, and a magnetic line must be tangential to it. PQ and RS are surfaces on which these boundary conditions are satisfied, so that if perfect conductors with plane surfaces are introduced into the field in such a way that their plane faces coincide with PQ and RS, the field between them is undisturbed. Thus the field configuration of Fig. 5-3 is obtained. The arrows indicate the direction of the field at an instant of time; on the next half-cycle, these directions will be reversed.

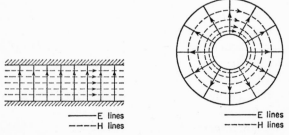

(Left) FIG. 5-3   Parallel-plate transmission line. (Right) FIG. 5-4   Coaxial transmission line.

This mode of propagation is called the *transverse electromagnetic mode*, or *TEM mode*, because both the electric and magnetic fields are transverse. The plane wave of Fig. 5-2 was, of course, propagating with the speed of light. The parallel-plate TEM mode of Fig. 5-3 also travels with the speed of light, for the wave in the region between the plates has not been disturbed in any way by their introduction. TEM waves can propagate in a variety of structures, but there must always be two separate conductors present. Such systems are called *transmission lines*. Figures 4-4, 5, and 6 show the field configurations in cross sections of the commonest types of transmission line. Figure 5-4 is the *coaxial line*, commonly in use for transmitting radio-frequency signals. Figure 5-5 illustrates the *parallel-wire line;* this is rarely used in practice, but is convenient for teaching purposes. Figure 5-6 shows a fairly new kind of trans-

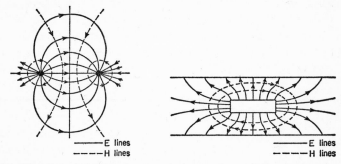

—— E lines
- - - H lines

—— E lines
- - - H lines

(Left) FIG. 5-5 Parallel-wire transmission line. (Right) FIG. 5-6 Strip transmission line.

mission line, the *strip line*, consisting of a live strip between two larger plates at earth potential. Notice that in all these lines the electric and magnetic fields are always in the transverse plane, i.e., the plane of the paper; they are always mutually perpendicular; and the electric lines are always perpendicular, the magnetic lines always tangential, to the conducting surfaces. In all these structures the velocity of the wave is equal to that of light.

Positions in the transverse plane of the parallel-plate line may be expressed in terms of the Cartesian coordinates x and y, with z perpendicular to the paper. The field components may then be written

$$E_y = E_0 \sin (\omega t - \beta z) \Big\rbrace$$
$$H_x = H_0 \sin (\omega t - \beta z) \Big\rbrace \qquad (5\text{-}1)$$

The waves have no variation in the x and y directions, so that E_y and H_x are functions of t and z only. The phase velocity is ω/β, and this is to be equal to c, the velocity of light. Hence

$$\beta = \omega/c \qquad (5\text{-}2)$$

According to equation 5-2, there is always a real value of β for any value of ω. This means that for any value of ω, however small, a TEM wave can propagate; this holds too for any other two-conductor system. This can be seen also in a physical way, for in showing how the configuration of Fig. 5-3 can be obtained from that of Fig. 5-2, nothing was said about the frequency, and clearly the frequency does not matter: the construction can, in principle, be carried out in the same way whatever the frequency may be.

§ 57. The TEM wave is not the only possible wave that can be supported by a two-conductor structure; there are other field configurations which satisfy the boundary conditions. One such is illustrated in Fig. 5-7; the field lines in the transverse plane and in a

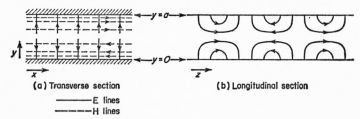

(a) Transverse section   (b) Longitudinal section

———— E lines
– – – – H lines

FIG. 5-7   Parallel plates supporting a waveguide mode.

section parallel to the direction of propagation are shown separately; in this case the electric field has a component in the z direction. This is necessary because a line of force must be continuous, and the reversal of sign shown in Fig. 5-7(a) on going from the top of the guide to the bottom would be impossible if the lines did not curve round into the z dimension.

The z component of electric field, E_z, is zero at the top and bottom surfaces, where $y = a$ and $y = 0$ respectively, and is a maximum at the mid-height, $y = a/2$. Thus E_z is proportional to $\sin ky$, where k

is a constant such that $ka = \pi$ or 180°. E_y and H_x, on the other hand, have maxima at $y = 0$, $y = a$, and are zero at $y = a/2$, and so are proportional to cos ky. The field components are also oscillatory in the z direction, and oscillatory with time. Notice also that E_y is a maximum or minimum when $E_z = 0$, and E_y is 0 when E_z is a maximum or minimum, i.e., E_y and E_z differ in phase by 90° or $\pi/2$. H_x is in phase with E_y. Such a mode is called an *E mode*, the *E* denoting that there is a longitudinal electric field component. It is also called a *transverse magnetic mode*, or *TM mode*, since the magnetic field is transverse but not the electric.

The field components are given by

$$\left.\begin{array}{l} E_z = E_0 \sin ky \sin (\omega t - \beta z) \\[2mm] E_y = -\dfrac{\beta}{k} E_0 \cos ky \cos (\omega t - \beta z) \\[2mm] H_x = \dfrac{\omega \epsilon_0}{k} E_0 \cos ky \cos (\omega t - \beta z) \\[2mm] E_x = H_y = H_z = 0 \end{array}\right\} \tag{5-3}$$

These expressions are readily seen to behave according to the above descriptions. The quantity ϵ_0 is called the *permittivity of free space.*

The constant k has to satisfy the condition that sin $ka = 0$, so that

$$ka = n\pi \tag{5-4}$$

where n is an integer. Thus for a given waveguide, for which there is a definite value of a, there are an infinite number of values of k for which the boundary conditions can be satisfied. Now, it can also be shown that

$$k^2 = \frac{\omega^2}{c^2} - \beta^2 \tag{5-5}$$

c being the velocity of light *in vacuo*, so that corresponding to each value of n, and hence of k, there is, at a given frequency, a value of β. These values of k are called *eigenvalues;* some writers prefer to use the term eigenvalue for the values of β. Not all the possible values of k correspond to propagating modes. If k is greater than ω/c, β^2 is given as negative by equation 5-5. Thus β is an imaginary quantity, and it can be shown that this corresponds to a rapid attenuation of the wave; the wave is evanescent.

For propagation, β^2 must be positive. This is the case for only a finite number of modes. For a given mode there is a value of frequency such that $\beta = 0$; for greater values of frequency, β^2 is positive and propagation takes place, while for smaller values of frequency the mode cannot propagate. The waveguide is then said to be *cut off* for the mode in question; the frequency at which $\beta = 0$ is called the *cut-off frequency*.

As well as the E modes, there are *H modes*, i.e., modes in which the magnetic field, but not the electric, has a longitudinal component. Then the electric field is transverse, and these modes are also called *transverse electric modes*, or *TE modes*. These also exhibit the cut-off property, and in this respect TE and TM modes differ from TEM modes which do not cut off, but propagate at all frequencies—or one might say that they cut off at zero frequency.

§ 58. Waveguides and transmission lines are used for conveying signals, i.e., waves which carry information. If more than one mode propagates in the guide, they interfere with each other, and the information is distorted. For most practical purposes, therefore, only one mode must be able to propagate. In the case of transmission lines, which are two-conductor systems, the mode is the TEM mode; transmission lines are used at frequencies such that all the TE and TM modes are cut off, i.e., at the higher radio frequencies, a few hundred Mc/s or perhaps a thousand or two Mc/s.* At sufficiently high frequencies, however, when TE and TM modes are able to propagate, transmission lines of convenient size become unsuitable. The TE or TM modes are then exploited, but the TEM mode must be suppressed. In one-conductor systems, TEM modes do not propagate, and when the dimensions are small enough, at a given frequency, only one mode can propagate.

The simplest kind of waveguide in regular use is the *rectangular guide*, illustrated in Fig. 5-8. The field configurations are illustrated for the mode whose cut-off frequency is the lowest and which can therefore exist in the absence of all the others. It is seen that the magnetic field has a z component, and so the mode is an H mode. The field components are given by

* Mc/s, or megacycles per second: 1 Mc/s = 10^6 cycles per second.

GUIDED WAVES   89

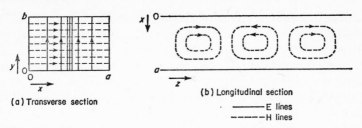

(a) Transverse section

(b) Longitudinal section

———— E lines
– – – – H lines

FIG. 5-8 H_{10} mode of a rectangular waveguide.

$$
\left.
\begin{aligned}
E_y &= E_0 \sin kx \sin (\omega t - \beta z) \\
H_z &= \frac{kE_0}{\omega \mu_0} \cos kx \cos (\omega t - \beta z) \\
H_x &= -\frac{\beta E_0}{\omega \mu_0} \sin kx \sin (\omega t - \beta z) \\
E_x &= E_z = H_y = 0
\end{aligned}
\right\}
\qquad (5\text{-}6)
$$

where k is given by equation 5-5. Also, for this mode, $k = \pi/a$, which is a special case of a mode having $k = n\pi/a$, with n put equal to 1. This figure, 1, determines the variation in the x direction, and so helps to characterize the mode. In the y direction, the variation is of the form $\begin{Bmatrix} \cos \\ \sin \end{Bmatrix} m\pi y/b$, with $m = 0$; this figure, 0, also helps to characterize the mode. Thus the mode is completely identified by the symbol H and the two numbers 0 and 1, and we call it the H_{10} mode.

Figure 5-9 shows the behavior of the phase constant with frequency for a typical waveguide mode. Such curves obtain for all

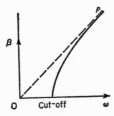

FIG. 5-9   Phase constant of a typical waveguide mode.

modes when the guide consists of an empty metal tube of some kind. If the tube is modified in some way, e.g., by loading it periodically or by inserting rods of other materials than metal, the curve is considerably modified in form. There are real values of β only for values of ω above the cut-off value, for the empty tube. When a rod of dielectric having a suitable value of dielectric constant is inserted into a metal tube of circular cross section, the ω-β curve of the waveguide so formed bulges into values of ω below the cut-off value; well away from cut-off, however, this guide behaves normally. When there is a bulge, there is a region of the curve where the slope, and therefore $d\omega/d\beta$, is negative, corresponding to a backward wave, i.e., a wave in which the phase and group velocities are oppositely directed, so that while energy flows away from the generator, the wavefronts move towards the generator. The line OP, passing through the origin, is the line $\omega/\beta = c$, and is approached asymptotically by all modes at high frequencies in the case of a metal-tube guide. Modes in loaded guides behave similarly, but ω/β approaches a value less than c at high frequencies.

The quantity ω/β is the phase velocity v_φ and becomes infinite at cut-off, decreasing with increasing velocity till it reaches the value c at infinity. The group velocity v_g is $d\omega/d\beta$ and is zero at cut-off, increasing with frequency till it reaches the value c at infinity. It is a curious fact that, for any waveguide consisting an empty metal tube, $v_\varphi v_g = c^2$. This relation does not hold, however, for other kinds of waveguide.

For the TEM mode, there is no cut-off. The constant k is zero, and equation 5-5 then gives $\omega/\beta = c$. This is the equation of the straight line OP in Fig. 5-9. The slope of this line is $d\omega/d\beta = c$ for all ω. Thus for the TEM mode as well as for the TE and TM modes, $v_\varphi v_g = c^2$.

§ 59. When it is desired to use a waveguide in a single mode, and other modes are able to propagate, it is necessary to take some care over the manner of excitation. At some point along the length it is necessary to set up the field pattern, over the whole cross section, appropriate to the desired mode. Any further fields, not conforming to this pattern, can be analyzed into a number of normal modes, and if these are able to propagate, they will; it is therefore important to generate just the values of field components proper to the desired mode. This is the same principle as is described in § 32.

Conversely, mode filters can be designed to remove certain modes and leave others. This is done, in general, by inserting devices into the guide which do not disturb the fields of the desired modes, but in which currents are excited by the other modes. It is arranged that these currents cause ohmic heating, thus extracting energy from the waves. The helix guide, to be discussed in § 62, can be regarded as a mode filter.

When only a single mode is able to propagate, more or less any exciting field will set it up. What happens in this case is that a number of modes are excited, corresponding to the modal analysis of the excitation, but all except one are evanescent, and a short way along the guide the evanescent modes have died out. The energy fed into these modes is either converted into the propagating mode or reflected into the generator. The mode conversion effect arises because of the presence of probes in the guide to excite it; these departures from uniformity of the guide permit coupling between the modes. The region near the source, where the spatial response is sorting itself out, is analogous to the initial behavior of the rope in § 3, where the temporal response is sorting itself out.

§ 60. Not only do electromagnetic fields travel in the space enclosed by the metal waveguide, but currents flow in the metal itself. These may be regarded as generated by the magnetic fields tangential to the walls, which excite currents such that at any point the current flow is perpendicular to the magnetic field lines. Alternatively, one may think of the magnetic fields as being set up by the currents. However one may choose to look at it, the fact is that currents and magnetic fields go together, and in the presence of a conductor you can't have one without the other. Figure 5-10 shows the lines of current flow, at a given instant, corresponding to the field patterns of Fig. 5-8. These currents flow on the *insides* of the guide walls, and form closed loops which are completed on the bottom surface (not shown in the diagram). At any point on the surface of the guide wall, the current line is perpendicular to the magnetic field line.

The current flow all takes place in a very thin layer of metal near

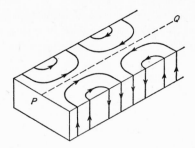

FIG. 5-10   Lines of current flow for a rectangular waveguide in the H_{10} mode.

the inside surface. This is again a question of skin depth, discussed in §§ 16 and 63; the thickness of metal in which current effectively flows is of the order of the skin depth. From equation 2-2, the skin depth for copper, out of which waveguides are commonly made, is

$$d = 3.82 \cdot 10^{-6} \sqrt{\lambda_0} \text{ meter}$$

where λ_0 is the free-space wavelength in meters. At a typical microwave frequency, λ_0 might be 3 cm = 0.03 meter. Then $d = 6.6 \cdot 10^{-7}$ meter = $6.6 \cdot 10^{-5}$ cm, which is very thin. Thus the metal walls of the guide can be quite thin without affecting its performance.

If *slots* are cut in the waveguide wall, the lines of current flow will in general be interrupted. Energy will radiate through the slots into space (indeed, some aerials are based on this principle), and the field patterns in the guide will be distorted because of the distortion of the lines of flow of the accompanying currents. However, if the slots are cut in such a way as not to cut across lines of current flow, no radiation occurs, and the wave travels along the guide unchanged. In Fig. 5-10, the line PQ is the center line of a broad face of the guide. For the H_{10} mode, it is seen that the current lines at the center line lie along PQ. Thus a narrow slit along PQ does not interfere with the current flow. This provides a means of inserting a probe into the guide to make observations on the waves, without disturbing the waves.

§ 61. A very important piece of microwave equipment is the standing-wave meter, which is used to measure reflections. It is incorporated in an experimental microwave system to observe standing waves set up by reflections at imperfect junctions of one length of guide to another, or at junctions of waveguides to various pieces of equipment. Standing waves are illustrated in Fig. 4-2 for the case of a unit reflection coefficient; in this case there are nodes. When the reflection coefficient is less than 1, the amplitude of the standing wave varies between a minimum and a maximum value, but is never zero. If the amplitude of the incident wave is 1 and of the reflected wave is r, the maximum amplitude of the standing wave is $1 + r$ and the minimum is $1 - r$. The ratio of the maximum to the minimum is $(1 + r)/(1 - r)$. This is called the *voltage standing wave ratio*, or VSWR, and is measured directly by a *standing-wave meter*, which is a probe moving in a slot along the line PQ of Fig. 5-10.

The probe is a short stub of wire which projects through the slot into the interior of the waveguide. This wire continues outside the guide as the core of a coaxial line. Currents are induced in the wire by the fields in the waveguide, the current amplitude being proportional to the electric field strength at the position of the probe. The currents give rise to the TEM mode in the coaxial line, and this is detected by some suitable apparatus.

The standing-wave meter is thus a device for measuring reflection coefficients; from the VSWR, r is readily obtained. Since the measurement of the VSWR depends on the interference of the reflected wave with the incident wave, the device is also an interferometer. In principle, it can also be used to measure wavelength, since this is twice the distance between successive maxima or minima; the determination of wavelength would not be very accurate, however, since the positions of the maxima and minima are not very precise.

§ 62. Because the conductivity of the waveguide walls is not infinite, i.e., because there is some resistance to the flow of current, energy is lost from the wave. The *attenuation* increases with increasing frequency, because the current generated in the wall is proportional to the rate of change of the magnetic flux linking the wall, and this rate of change is proportional to frequency. As the frequency is reduced, the attenuation from this cause decreases, until the frequency approaches the cut-off value. Below cut-off, the evanescent wave is attenuated rapidly, and so the attenuation rises steeply on approaching cut-off. The amplitude of the wave at a point z is proportional to $e^{-\alpha z}$, which decreases with increasing z; α is called the attenuation constant. The behavior of α with frequency for a typical waveguide mode is illustrated in Fig. 5-11; this behavior occurs for most modes of waveguides which consist of tubes of metal.

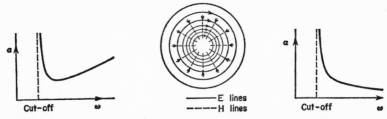

(Left) FIG. 5-11   Attenuation characteristic of a typical waveguide mode.
(Center) FIG. 5-12 H_{01} mode of a waveguide of circular cross section.
(Right) FIG. 5-13   Attenuation characteristic for an H_{0n} mode of a waveguide of circular cross section.

In the case of a guide of circular cross section, the modes of the H_{0n} family do not exhibit this behavior. The field pattern in the transverse plane for the H_{01} mode is illustrated in Fig. 5-12. For these modes the attenuation constant behaves as in Fig. 5-13, steadily decreasing with increasing frequency. The reason for this is that as the frequency increases, the energy in the wave concentrates closer in to the center of the guide; the fields near the walls become weaker, and so the currents generated are weaker.

By going to very high frequencies and large values of guide radius, very low attenuation can be obtained with the H_{01} mode, and in principle it would therefore appear that the guide of circular cross section might be useful for conveying information over large distances. The high frequency would permit a large number of communication channels, whereas with the coaxial lines that are used at present* the number of channels is limited by the fact that other modes start to propagate above a certain frequency.

There are, however, a number of technical difficulties to be overcome. For at the very high frequencies envisaged, a large number of modes are able to propagate, and at any imperfection in the

---

* Coaxial lines have just been developed capable of operating over a much greater frequency range than hitherto.

guide some of the power in the H_{01} mode will be converted into other modes. This not only causes loss of power in the H_{01} mode; it also leads to interference between the H_{01} and the unwanted modes, with consequent distortion of the information carried. Thus guides must be made as nearly perfect as possible, and provision must be made to remove power from any mode other than the H_{01}. It looks now as if the most likely solution is going to be to use *helix guide*.

The wall currents of the H_{0n} modes are circular; they travel in circular paths in the guide wall, perpendicular to the axis. For all other modes, the wall currents have components parallel to the axis. If the wall can be made to conduct in the direction perpendicular to the axis and not in the direction parallel to the axis, the wall currents of the H_{0n} modes will not be interfered with, and these modes will propagate just as well as in a guide with isotropic wall. For all other modes, the wall currents are interrupted, and the guide radiates.

The anisotropically conducting wall is achieved by a wire helix of very thin insulated wire and very small pitch. This conducts in a direction extremely close to the transverse direction, and not in the axial direction, as required. A jacket of lossy dielectric material surrounds the helix of wire (Fig. 5-14); this absorbs all energy radiated into it, so that all modes except those of the H_{0n} family are rapidly attenuated. The H_{02}, H_{03}, H_{04}, etc., modes are still able to propagate, and special mode filters need to be designed to remove them. The removal of unwanted modes will prevent interference and distortion of the signal, but there will still be a loss of power from the H_{01} mode into other modes at defects in the guide. The kinds of defects that

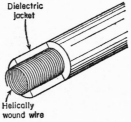

Dielectric jacket

Helically wound wire

FIG. 5-14   Helix guide.

are likely to occur are ellipticity and curvature of the guide; offsets and abrupt changes of direction of the axes at points where one length of guide is joined to another; changes of radius from one length of guide to another; and various imperfections in the windings and in the jacket material. These problems have been studied for a number of years in various European countries and in America, and are not yet all solved.

§ 63. Two-conductor waveguides are usually used in the TEM mode. For many purposes it is convenient to think in terms of the current in the conductors and the voltage between them, rather than in terms of the fields in the space between them. The two-conductor system is then called a transmission line, and the methods of electric circuit theory are used instead of field theory.

It will be simplest to think of the parallel-wire line, although the essential principles apply equally well to all types of line. There is a capacity between the two conductors, and since this is proportional to length it is convenient to work in terms of the *capacity per unit length*. It is perhaps less obvious that there is also an *inductance per unit length* associated with the wires. When a direct current flows in a wire, it sets up a magnetic field in the form of concentric lines of force around the wire. If an alternating current flows in the wire, it sets up a magnetic field which alternates, the lines of magnetic force collapsing into the wire and then expanding again, with the field in the opposite sense. This changing magnetic field induces electromotive forces in the wire which oppose the change of current. This is the property of inductance.

Let us now imagine the wire to be made up of a large number of concentric shells, or thin-walled tubes, the outer radius of one being equal to the inner radius of the next, so that all the tubes fit together to make the solid wire. It is only the magnetic lines of force outside a given shell which contribute to the inductance of that shell, so that the inductance is higher for a current element at the center of the wire than for one farther out, and is least for currents at the surface. Thus the flow of current is hindered by an inductive reactance which is least on the surface, and the current therefore flows more strongly the farther it is from the wire center.

Since the central parts of the wire are less effective than the periphery in conducting current, the effective resistance of the whole wire to alternating current is increased. This effect is called the *skin effect*, because at high frequencies the wire behaves as if the current flowed in a thin surface layer, or skin, of the wire. At frequencies up to some tens of megacycles per second, this is the most important effect of the inductance of a wire. At higher frequencies, however, where transmission lines are used, the inductive reactance of a wire becomes more important and the resistance is then relatively unimportant. It will therefore be permissible to consider transmission lines as having an inductance per unit length and a capacity per unit length, and to treat them as lossless.

The skin effect always comes into play when electromagnetic fields are associated with conductors. One may think of it from the point of view of the current, as here, or in terms of an evanescent wave, as in § 16. The *skin depth* was first thought of—and to this it owes its name—as a thickness of the "skin" of the conductor such that, if all the current flowed in the skin, with uniform density equal to that actually obtaining at the surface, the resistance would be equal to that actually observed.

The inductance per unit length, L, and the capacity per unit length, C, of a transmission line are not independent, and it can be shown that in fact $1/\sqrt{LC}$ is the velocity of light in the medium filling the line, i.e., $3\cdot10^{10}$ cm per second if the medium is vacuum or air. The wavelength is the velocity divided by the frequency, i.e.,

$$\lambda = 2\pi/\omega\sqrt{LC} \tag{5-7}$$

and the phase constant, which is $2\pi/\lambda$, is

$$\beta = \omega\sqrt{LC} \tag{5-8}$$

Another important quantity is

$$Z_0 = \sqrt{L/C} \tag{5-9}$$

which has the dimensions of an impedance and is called the *characteristic impedance*.

The voltage at any point on a line is

$$V = V_0 \cos(\omega t - \beta z + \varphi) \tag{5-10}$$

and the current is

$$I = I_0 \cos (\omega t - \beta z + \theta) \qquad (5\text{-}11)$$

where φ and θ are phase angles. If a semi-infinite line is connected to a generator, the generator "sees" the characteristic impedance Z_0 (see Fig. 5-15). At the input end of the line, where $z = 0$, the voltage is the generator voltage, $= V_0 \cos \omega t$ if φ is put equal to zero.

(Left) FIG. 5-15   (Right) FIG. 5-16

Z_0 appears as a resistance, so that I and V are in phase. Then $\theta = 0$, and at any point on the line

$$\left.\begin{array}{l} V = V_0 \cos (\omega t - \beta z) \\ I = I_0 \cos (\omega t - \beta z) \\ V/I = Z_0 \end{array}\right\} \qquad (5\text{-}12)$$

If at some point the line is broken, and a resistance equal to Z_0 is connected across the ends, as in Fig. 5-16, the current and voltage on the line at the end are in the correct relation for this resistance, so that there is no reflection. The generator sees no difference between a line terminated by its characteristic impedance and an infinite line. A line terminated by its characteristic impedance is said to be *correctly terminated*.

§ 64. When a line is incorrectly terminated, i.e., terminated by an impedance Z_T different from its characteristic impedance, the current and voltage on the line, before it is broken, are not in the right relationship to suit the terminating impedance. There is then a reflection. To look at it another way, the line is happy with waves traveling on it in either direction. The relative amplitudes of the forward and backward waves must be such as to satisfy the boundary conditions at the end of the line, i.e., that the ratio of V to I must be Z_T. We shall only consider the case where Z_T is a resistance.

The forward wave has voltage and current given by

$$\left.\begin{array}{l} V = V_1 \cos (\omega t - \beta z) \\ I = I_1 \cos (\omega t - \beta z) = \dfrac{V_1}{Z_0} \cos (\omega t - \beta z) \end{array}\right\} \qquad (5\text{-}13)$$

while the backward wave has

$$V = V_2 \cos (\omega t + \beta z)$$
$$I = -I_2 \cos (\omega t + \beta z) = -\frac{V_2}{Z_0} \cos (\omega t + \beta z) \Bigg\} \quad (5\text{-}14)$$

The minus sign before I_2 is due to the fact that the current is regarded as positive when flowing in the opposite direction. The total voltage at any point is

$$V = V_1 \cos (\omega t - \beta z) + V_2 \cos (\omega t + \beta z)$$

and the total current is

$$I = \frac{1}{Z_0} \{V_1 \cos (\omega t - \beta z) - V_2 \cos (\omega t + \beta z)\}$$

Hence the impedance at any point is

$$\frac{V}{I} = \frac{V_1 \cos (\omega t - \beta z) + V_2 \cos (\omega t + \beta z)}{\dfrac{1}{Z_0} \{V_1 \cos (\omega t - \beta z) - V_2 \cos (\omega t + \beta z)\}}$$

and this is to equal Z_T at the end of the line, where $z = l$. Putting $z = l$ and rearranging, we obtain readily

$$\frac{V_2 \cos (\omega t + \beta l)}{V_1 \cos (\omega t - \beta l)} = \frac{Z_T - Z_0}{Z_T + Z_0}$$

Now, $\cos (\omega t \pm \beta l)$ is a function which is periodic in time, with a phase angle $\pm \beta l$. If we take the time average of the squares of the voltages (because the time average of the voltage itself is zero) and then take the square roots of the averages, we obtain the root mean square voltages, $\overline{V}_1$ and $\overline{V}_2$, and

$$\frac{\overline{V}_2}{\overline{V}_1} = \frac{Z_T - Z_0}{Z_T + Z_0} \quad (5\text{-}15)$$

$\overline{V}_2/\overline{V}_1$ is the *voltage reflection coefficient.*

Instead of a lumped impedance, Z_T may be the characteristic impedance of another line connected to the first. Suppose that the line starts with vacuum between the conductors, and that from some point of its length onwards the medium is a dielectric with dielectric constant ϵ and permeability μ times that of free space. Then $L_2 = \mu L_1$ and $C_2 = \epsilon C_1$. If the velocity in the first line is v, that in the second is $v/\sqrt{\epsilon\mu}$. The impedances are $Z_0 = \sqrt{L_1/C_1}$ and $Z_T = \sqrt{L_2/C_2} = Z_0\sqrt{\mu/\epsilon}$. The reflection coefficient is

$$\frac{\sqrt{\mu/\epsilon} - 1}{\sqrt{\mu/\epsilon} + 1} = \frac{\sqrt{\mu} - \sqrt{\epsilon}}{\sqrt{\mu} + \sqrt{\epsilon}}$$

If $\mu = 1$, the velocity is $v/\sqrt{\epsilon}$, and the refractive index is $\sqrt{\epsilon}$. The reflection coefficient is now $(1 - \sqrt{\epsilon})/(1 + \sqrt{\epsilon})$ which may be compared with equation 2-7; the latter only holds if the media on either side of the boundary have the same permeability.

§ 65. For some purposes it is possible to treat certain kinds of waveguides as transmission lines. These are the waveguides consisting of a tube of metal of some sort, with homogeneous filling, and there must be only a single mode propagating. The value of the transverse component of electric field, at any point in the cross section, is then in a certain ratio to the magnetic field at that point. This ratio is of the nature of an impedance multiplied by an undetermined constant, which we may put equal to 1 for convenience. Then formulae for reflection coefficients in such waveguides will be the same as in transmission lines, and certain problems concerning waveguide systems can be worked out by analogy in terms of transmission-line theory. This should be borne in mind in the further discussion of lines.

In many kinds of waveguide in modern use, the cross section is not homogeneously filled, and the ratio of electric to magnetic field varies from point to point in the cross section. It is then impossible to define a characteristic impedance, and transmission-line theory cannot be used.

§ 66. If an abrupt transition is made in the value of the Z_0 of a line, there is a reflection. Such reflections are undesirable for two reasons; there is a loss of power—the reflected energy is lost to the forward wave—and the energy which is reflected may get back into the generator and cause frequency instability.

One way to overcome this trouble is to use a *quarter-wave transformer*. The transition is made in two steps, a quarter of a wavelength apart, the reflections being the same at both steps. The wave reflected from the second step travels a half-wavelength farther than the wave reflected from the first step, so that the two reflected waves are in antiphase. They interfere destructively to give a zero net reflection; the transition is then said to be *matched*. Matching is obtained at only one frequency; away from this frequency, the distance between the two steps is no longer a quarter-wavelength, and there is a reflected wave. A small reflection coefficient over a wide band of frequencies can be obtained by making the transition in a number of steps, each separated from the next by a quarter-wavelength at the center of the frequency band. If the reflection coefficients at the steps, taken in order, are in the ratios of the binomial coefficients (1:2:1, 1:3:3:1, 1:4:6:4:1, etc.), the overall reflection coefficient can be shown to be $r \cos^n (2\pi x/\lambda)$, where r is the reflection coefficient that would be found if the transition were made in a single jump, x is the distance between one discontinuity and the next, λ is the wavelength, and $n + 1$ is the number of steps. When $x = \lambda/4$, $\cos (2\pi x/\lambda) = 0$, and for values of x that depart quite widely from $\lambda/4$, the value of $\cos (2\pi x/\lambda)$ remains fairly small. $\cos^n (2\pi x/\lambda)$ is much smaller, and the higher n the higher the range of frequencies over which it remains small. Thus matching can be obtained over a wide frequency range. This method of minimizing the reflection coefficients is called *binomial matching*.

The binomial matching technique is also used in optics in the *blooming of lenses*. On the surface of a lens a layer of suitable transparent material is laid, of a thickness equal to a quarter-wavelength in the middle of the visible spectrum. More than one layer may be used to increase the range of colors over which matching is obtained. The materials used are chosen to have refractive indices which give suitable reflection coefficients. In this way all the light from an incident beam is caused to pass through the lens. In photography, loss of light by reflection at the front and back surfaces of the camera lens can be substantial, and to admit a given amount of light to the camera either the aperture or the exposure time must be increased to make up for this. With a bloomed lens, smaller apertures or shorter exposures can be used. Also, without blooming, light which is reflected at the lens surfaces traverses the lens more than once before emerging, and arrives at the film out of focus, causing fogging.

§ 67. We saw in § 57 that when a waveguide is excited in a certain mode at a certain frequency, only a single definite value of β, and therefore of wavelength, is possible. Now let us imagine that two perfectly conducting plane surfaces are placed in the waveguide, perpendicular to its axis, an integral number of half-wavelengths apart. Reflection will take place at the planes, and a backward and a forward wave will be set up, giving standing waves. Only if the distance between the planes is exactly an integral number of half-wavelengths apart can the boundary conditions be satisfied at both surfaces. Looking at it another way, given the *rectangular cavity* with metallic surfaces, a wave can only be excited if the wavelength is one of a number of values such that the length of the cavity is an integral number of half-wavelengths. Since the wavelength is dependent on the frequency, this means that the cavity will resonate at a number of frequencies which will be dependent on the cavity dimensions.

Cavities may be of any of a variety of shapes, but two of the commonest are the rectangular and the circular cylindrical cavities. They find application in three main fields—in controlling the frequencies of oscillators, in measuring frequency, and in the measurement of the properties of materials.

Frequency is measured by means of a *cavity wavemeter*. This consists of a cavity coupled to a waveguide, e.g., by a small hole in their common wall. The cavity can be tuned in some way; usually one end consists of a piston which can be moved in or out by means of a screw. When the cavity is correctly tuned, it resonates, and from a reading of the position of the piston the resonance frequency can be determined; this is evidently the frequency of the waves under observation. The resonance of the cavity is observed by coupling energy out through a second small hole and feeding it to a detector. At wavelengths less than a centimeter or so the cavity dimensions are small, and the coupling holes are relatively large. This lowers the Q of the cavity, and the measurement becomes less precise.

The resonance frequency of a cavity depends on the materials contained in the interior. If the cavity is filled with a gas, or if a small piece of dielectric or magnetic material is inserted, a small shift of the resonance frequency takes place. The frequency shift can be calculated in terms of the property being measured by means of perturbation theory, and the result can be used to determine the value of the property from a measurement of the frequency shift.

Dielectric and magnetic losses can also be determined by measuring the change of Q on inserting the specimen.

§ 68. A resonant cavity can be regarded as a finite length of waveguide, closed at both ends. The electric field at the ends must be zero to satisfy the boundary conditions, so that the impedances at the ends are zero. The terminating planes are thus short circuits. In Fig. 5-17 the field configurations are shown for the case of a circular

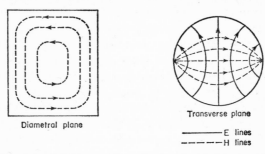

Diametral plane

Transverse plane

———— E lines
— — — —H lines

FIG. 5-17   Field lines of H_{111} mode of cylindrical cavity.

cylindrical cavity oscillating in the H_{111} mode. A short-circuited transmission line will also resonate if excited at the correct frequency. So, too, can an open-circuited line. These lines will resonate at frequencies such that they are an integral number of half-wavelengths long. A line also resonates when open-circuited at one end and short-circuited at the other, if it is an odd number of quarter-wavelengths long. The voltage and current distributions for this last case are illustrated in Fig. 5-18. At the input to the line,

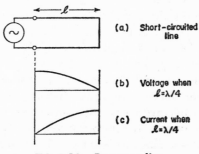

(a)   Short-circuited line

(b)   Voltage when $\ell = \lambda/4$

(c)   Current when $\ell = \lambda/4$

FIG. 5-18   Resonant line.

i.e., at the output terminals of the generator, the ratio of voltage to current is infinite, and the line appears as an open circuit to the generator.

If the line is not a quarter-wavelength long, the impedance seen by the generator will depend on the line length. If the line is between a quarter- and a half-wavelength long, it appears as a capacitive reactance varying from infinity (zero capacity or open circuit) at $l = \lambda/4$ to zero (infinite capacity or short circuit) at $l = \lambda/2$. If the length is less than a quarter-wavelength, the line appears as an inductive reactance ranging from infinity at $l = \lambda/4$ to zero at $l = 0$. Thus at a single frequency any desired reactance can be obtained with a stub of line less than half a wavelength long.

Such a stub can be used to match a line to its termination (which may be, for example, a resonant cavity or a dipole aerial). If the load impedance Z_T is purely resistive, it can be matched by the quarter-wave transformer PQ (Fig. 5-19). If it has also a reactive compo-

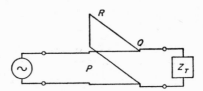

FIG. 5-19   Matching a terminated line.

nent, the impedance at Q can be made to appear purely resistive if a stub QR is connected as shown, the length of QR being chosen to give a reactance equal and opposite to the reactive component of Z_T.

§ 69. While we have been talking mainly of electromagnetic waveguides until now, there are many other kinds, as was pointed out at the beginning of this chapter. The analogy between an organ pipe and a transmission line is apparent on comparing Figs. 3-12 and 5-18. Figure 3-12 shows the velocity of the air particles in the organ pipe. If the velocity times the area of cross section of the pipe is compared with the current on the line, the open end of the pipe is an *acoustic short circuit*. The pressure differential, i.e., the difference of pressure between a point in the pipe and the external atmosphere, is then analogous to the transmission-line voltage, and the ratio of pressure differential to velocity times area is an *acoustic characteristic impedance.* The principle of duality (§ 27) can be invoked here, and velocity times area can be compared to voltage and pressure differential to current. An open end is then an acoustic open circuit, and the characteristic impedance is the ratio of velocity X area to pressure differential. Results of calculations on either basis will be the same when translated back into acoustic terms.

The above paragraph applies to an organ pipe in which the pressure and velocity are constant over the cross section. With a pipe of sufficiently large radius, it is possible to generate modes in which the pressure amplitude and velocity amplitude are functions of position in the transverse plane. These modes cut off at a certain frequency, just like modes in electromagnetic waveguides. In this respect the organ pipe is again analogous to a transmission line, which we saw in § 57 can support waveguide modes at sufficiently high frequencies. In normal use, as with transmission lines, the radius of the pipe is sufficiently small to permit propagation only of the "transmission-line" mode.

Kundt's tube is an acoustic device, working on the same principle as the cavity wavemeter (§ 67), and is used for measuring the velocity of sound in a gas. It consists of a rod clamped at its center, which carries a light plate at one end. This plate forms a piston fitting into a tube (Fig. 5-20). The rod is excited in a longitudinal mode by

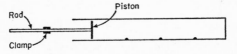

FIG. 5-20   Kundt's tube.

stroking with a cloth, and the frequency is determined by its length. The plate is caused to vibrate by the rod, setting up vibrations in the gas column in the tube. The position of the piston is adjusted until the gas column resonates. The tube contains a small quantity of fine powder, and at resonance this collects at the nodes, being blown away from the antinodes. The distance between one heap of powder and the next is a half-wavelength. Thus the frequency and the wavelength in the gas are known, and so the velocity in the gas is obtained. The adjustment of the piston is similar to the adjustment of the microwave cavity wavemeter, although in this case the frequency is known, whereas the microwave instrument measures the frequency.

Rods of elastic materials, such as metals, also behave as waveguides or transmission lines. They are commonly used in torsional modes, and the simplest mode is one in which the whole cross section twists in the same way at the same time. This mode does not cut off, and so is analogous to the TEM mode of an electromagnetic line. At higher frequencies, different regions of the cross section can twist in different directions, and patterns of displacement over the cross section are obtained which present similar features to the fields in the electromagnetic waveguide of circular cross section. Longitudinal vibrations are also possible, in which the motion is parallel to the axis of the rod. These mechanical waveguides are used in wave filters (§ 74).

A stretched string can be compared to a transmission line, with certain limitations. The wave on the string must always have the same velocity, and in this respect it is analogous to the TEM mode of the electromagnetic line. The waveguide modes of the electromagnetic line, however, necessarily have field components with nodes and antinodes in definite positions in the guide cross section. No analogue of this can exist on an ideal string because this is a one-dimensional structure. Thus a string might be regarded as a transmission line whose first waveguide mode has an infinite cut-off frequency. The string is, of course, necessarily clamped at both ends. If we regard the tension in the string as analogous to the pressure in an organ pipe and to the voltage of an electromagnetic line, and the transverse velocity of an element of the string as analogous to current, we can define an impedance of the string, and this is infinite at the clamped ends, which are therefore analogous to open circuits. If the clamp at the end of a string is not perfect, it behaves as a finite impedance, and the string is then analogous to a line terminated in an arbitrary impedance. Analogously to the organ pipe mentioned above, the clamped ends can be regarded as short circuits by virtue of the principle of duality.

§ 70. Electromagnetic waveguides are often used to feed aerials, and in Chapter 4 we saw that the determination of the radiation pattern is essentially a diffraction problem. The beam from the open end of a waveguide is not highly directional because the aperture is not large compared with a wavelength. If the guide is terminated in a horn, the aperture is larger, and the directivity is improved. Also, the reflection back along the guide is reduced, i.e., the guide is better matched to the free space into which the energy radiates—the horn is, in effect, a matching device. The impedance of a waveguide depends on its dimensions, and when these become large, it approaches that of free space. Thus the open end of a horn is better matched to free space than is the end of a waveguide without a horn, and the horn provides a gradual transition between the waveguide impedance and the impedance of the open end of the horn.

The same principle applies with musical instruments such as horns, trombones, bugles, etc., which terminate in a flared opening which matches acoustic waves in the instrument to those in the open air. The effect of a mute in such an instrument is to reduce the area of the orifice, which partly nullifies the matching property of the flare. Radiation into the air is then less efficient; also, the effect of the mute is different at different frequencies, so that the amplitude distribution of the overtones is modified. In this way the tonal quality as well as the loudness is modified.

§ 71. Waveguides usually have dimensions of the same order of size as the wavelength of the wave that is guided, and the limitations on their use are imposed by the mechanical problems of making them, not by the nature of the wave concerned. In recent years, *optical waveguides* have been developed, consisting of fine fibers of some transparent material. These behave to light waves just as does a dielectric rod to microwaves. The electromagnetic wave guided by a dielectric rod does not travel wholly in the rod; a fair proportion of the energy travels in the space surrounding the rod. For optical applications this is undesirable, as we shall see in a moment, and the wave must be confined somehow to the interior of the fiber. A metallic coating is not suitable because at optical frequencies the loss would be too great (§ 16), but it has been found that the wave can be suitably confined if a thin layer of another dielectric material is used to coat the fiber. Waves radiating in the radial direction "see" two reflecting surfaces half a wavelength apart. The reflected waves reinforce each other to give a strong reflection, so that very little energy leaks out. The subject of the behavior and applications of these light-carrying fibers is known as *fiber optics*.

It is possible to bundle together a large number of such fibers, in each of which light travels with no interference from the light in the other fibers. If the positions of the fibers, relative to each other, are the same at both ends, a picture focused onto one end of the bundle will be transmitted to the other end, where it can be observed. Since the fiber bundle can be twisted about, and the light in a single fiber will be transmitted round the bends, these devices can be used to make observations in places otherwise inaccessible. They are likely to be widely used in the future in medicine, providing a means of examining internal organs such as the heart, lungs, stomach, and lower intestine without major surgery. They may similarly be used to inspect parts of machinery inaccessible to a man (like the engines of modern motor cars), or the interiors of pipes. They may provide a means of watching what is happening in another room in a building (e.g., the nursery) much cheaper than with closed-circuit television. Finally, they have possibilities as coding devices. A picture or writing focused on one end can be scrambled by rearranging the fibers at the other end in a random way. The scrambled picture can then be conveyed as a print or by television and unscrambled at the other end by a similar device. In the scrambled form the picture is secure from observation by anyone not equipped with the right scrambling device.

§ 72. In the ears of mammals a number of the features described in this chapter are exploited. Figure 5-21 shows a highly schematic sketch of a mammalian ear. The sound first enters a more or less

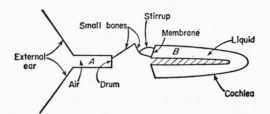

FIG. 5-21   Mammalian ear.

straight, uniform tube A containing air at atmospheric pressure. At the outer end of this tube is the external ear. In man, the function of the external ear is entirely decorative, but in many animals it is in the form of a horn, and performs the same matching function as the flare on a musical instrument. This may readily be seen on examining the family dog or cat.

At the inner end of the passage A is the eardrum, a membrane which closes the passage. The drum is connected to a series of three small bones, the last of which is called the stirrup from its characteristic form. The stirrup is connected to a membrane which covers the entrance to the cochlea, B. This is a long, elaborately entwined tube (shown straightened out in Fig. 5-21) containing a liquid. In the center of the cochlea is a bony layer in which are the nerve endings which are stimulated by the sounds.

The tube A and the cochlea B form acoustic transmission lines. Their impedances differ because of the different media with which they are filled, and the small bones form an acoustic matching system exploiting, with modifications, the binomial principle. When it is remembered that the human ear can receive sounds over a frequency range from several tens of cycles per second to fifteen or more kilocycles per second, and comparable ranges for other animals, it will be realized what an excellent matching transformer these small bones provide. The drum is an essential element of this transformer, providing the coupling between the air tube A and the first small bone. If the eardrum is pierced, it cannot vibrate properly, just like a musical drum. This results in impaired hearing.

§ 73. Guided waves, it has been suggested,[*] are also made use of in the eyes of creatures, such as birds and the primates, which have color vision. In the retinas of the eyes of such creatures there are two kinds of light-sensitive elements, known as rods and cones, and it is the cones with which we are concerned here. Animals such as dogs, cats, horses, cows, and rats have only the rod receptors, and are unable to distinguish colors.

A cone of a human eye is shown, somewhat idealized, in Fig. 5-22. Light, focused by the lens, is incident on the retina from the right-

[*] A. C. Schroeder, "Theory on the Receptor Mechanism in Color Vision," Journal of the Optical Society of America, **50**, 945-949 (1960).

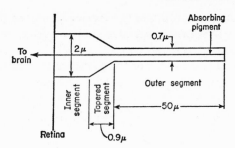

FIG. 5-22   Human retinal cone.

hand side of the diagram. The light thus focused, at the end of the inner segment of a particular cone, enters the inner segment, where it propagates more or less as a plane wave, because the inner segment is many wavelengths in diameter. The light then passes through the conical segment and enters the outer segment; the conical segment acts as a matching horn, as discussed in § 70. The diameter of the outer segment is not large compared with a wavelength, so that this segment acts as a dielectric-rod waveguide, similarly to the fibers discussed in § 69.

The diameter of the outer segment is such as to enable a small number of modes to propagate. Which these are, and their relative amplitudes, will depend on the frequency, and thus the color, of the light which is exciting the cone. According to the color, the modes will interfere to give different distributions of maxima and minima along the center of the outer segment, along which is a thread of absorbing pigment.

The suggestion is that the nerve cells which actually respond to the light are located at various positions along the absorbing pigment. Now, when a nerve is stimulated, a series of pulses travels along it, and the intensity of the stimulus is represented by the *frequency* of the pulses, whose amplitude remains constant. When a receptor in the cone is stimulated, it fires, and a train of pulses travels in each direction, one directly towards the retina and on to the brain, the other towards the outer end of the outer segment, where it is reflected and travels back towards the brain. Thus the brain receives two series of pulses, with a certain delay between them depending on the position of the receptor along the outer segment.

Similar pairs of series of pulses are received from all the receptors, and the patterns of pulses are analyzed by the brain; from these the color of the light is deduced.

That this is the mechanism of color vision is at present only a suggestion, and further investigations will be necessary to confirm it or otherwise. But the essentially guided-wave type of propagation in the outer segment can hardly be in doubt.

6   Topics in Network Theory

§ 74. The various kinds of waves, traveling in their various media, are affected by discontinuities in the media in different ways according to their frequency. This enables us to build *wave filters* which accept waves in a given frequency range and reject waves with frequencies outside the range. The electrical resonant circuits of §§ 26 and 27, for example, can be used to make simple band-pass or band-stop filters. Figure 6-1 shows such a circuit, its coil forming the pri-

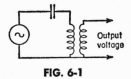

FIG. 6-1

mary of a transformer. Current in the primary generates an EMF in the secondary, and the terminal voltage of the secondary forms the output. When the primary current is high, so is the secondary voltage, which therefore shows the same behavior with frequency as does the primary current. The resonance curve of Fig. 3-1 is therefore applicable to the secondary voltage, and the filter responds to frequencies within the line-width, or *band-width* as it is called in radio.

Such a circuit is commonly used in radio sets; the generator is the aerial, and the desired signal is chosen by varying the capacity, and hence the resonance frequency, of the circuit. The output is fed to an electrode of a valve or transistor and amplified.

Filters are used for a variety of purposes in radio and communications engineering and radar. Sometimes it is desired to separate out one from a large number of signals, which is the task performed by the aerial tuning circuit of a radio receiver mentioned above. More elaborate filters are needed for waves that are modulated in various ways, to separate the modulation signal from the modulated signal.

§ 75. A wave is said to be *modulated* when its amplitude, phase, or frequency is modified by another wave. The wave that has been modulated is called a *carrier wave*. The function $A \cos \Omega t \cos (\omega t - \beta z)$ represents a wave of frequency $\omega/2\pi$, traveling in the z direction, its amplitude being $A \cos \Omega t$, with $\Omega \ll \omega$; $\omega/2\pi$ is the carrier frequency, and $\Omega/2\pi$ is the modulating frequency. Such a wave is said to be *amplitude modulated;* its amplitude varies with time. The function is illustrated in Fig. 6-2.

(Left) FIG. 6-2   Amplitude-modulated wave. (Right) FIG. 6-3   Frequency-modulated wave.

The function $A \cos [\omega_0 t + (a\omega_0/\Omega) \sin \Omega t - \beta z]$ represents a *frequency-modulated* wave (Fig. 6-3), where ω_0 is the carrier frequency, a is a constant $\ll 1$, and the frequency at any instant is the time derivative of the function in square brackets: $\omega = \omega_0 + a\omega_0 \cos \Omega t$. ω varies about the mean, ω_0, with frequency Ω. The amplitude is constant.

Waves modulated in these ways are used in radio transmission. The carrier, of frequency $\omega/2\pi$, is provided by an oscillator and amplifier, and fed to an aerial. At some stage in the process, a modulating signal is injected; this is obtained as an electrical signal from a microphone into which the current teen-age heart-throb is gently drooling. Filter circuits in the receiver separate out the modulating signal from the carrier, and correct for distortion arising out of imperfections in the apparatus, in order to produce at the loudspeaker a highly accurate imitation of the original sound picked up by the microphone.

An amplitude-modulated carrier, modulated by a single frequency Ω, can be shown by Fourier analysis to be made up of the
frequencies $\omega - \Omega$, ω, and $\omega + \Omega$. All these frequencies must be
accepted by the receiver, so the resonance of the aerial tuning cir-
cuit must not be too sharp. If the *sidebands* (i.e., $\omega \pm \Omega$) are lost
through too sharp tuning, only the carrier is received, and the
modulating signal cannot be filtered out from the carrier alone.
There is a parallel here with the Abbé theory of the microscope
(§ 54); the microscope which admits only the zeroth-order diffracted wave is analogous to the radio receiver which is so sharply
tuned as to admit only the carrier wave—in both cases the waves
which carry information are lost. In the speech or music which is
transmitted by a radio wave, all the frequencies up to a certain
value will be present; thus the carrier and sidebands cover a band
of frequencies, and ideally the input filter of the receiver should
have a response which is uniform over this band, and falls sharply
to zero outside the band to avoid interference from other signals.
Figure 6-4(a) shows the response of such an ideal *band-pass filter;*
the sort of filter response realizable in practice is shown in Fig.
6-4(b).

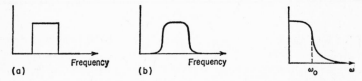

(a)   Frequency   (b)   Frequency ω_0 ω

(Left) FIG. 6-4   Response of (a) ideal and (b) practical band-pass filter.
(Right) FIG. 6-5   Response of maximally flat low-pass filter.

§ 76. Another important filter is the *low-pass filter*, illustrated in
Fig. 6-5. Functions such as those illustrated in Figs. 6-4 and 6-5 are
called *transfer functions*. They are properties of the filters and are independent of the input. In the case of a *two-port filter*, such as is
illustrated in Fig. 6-6, the transfer function enables us to calculate
the output from the pair of terminals (2) (the *output port*) when a
given input is applied to terminals (1) (the *input port*). In Fig. 6-6, the
input is taken to be a voltage varying with time; the variation is
given by the function $e(t)$. We could equally well have chosen a

current. The output is the *response function*, $r(t)$, which may be a current or a voltage. According to the nature of the input and response functions, the transfer function is given as an impedance, an admittance, or a dimensionless quantity.

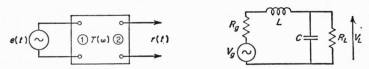

(Left) FIG. 6-6   Two-port network. (Right) FIG. 6-7   Low-pass filter

As an example of a transfer function, Fig. 6-7 shows a simple low-pass filter. R_g is the internal resistance of the generator, which we assume to give a constant voltage V_g at all frequencies. R_L is a load resistance, which may include, for example, the input resistance of a vacuum tube; in this case, the input capacity of the vacuum tube is included in C. The amplitude of the ratio of the output voltage to the input voltage is

$$\left|\frac{V_L}{V_g}\right| = \frac{R_L}{\sqrt{(R_L + R_g)^2 + \omega^2[L^2 + C^2R_L^2R_L^2 - 2LCR_g^2] + \omega^4 L^2 C^2 R_L^2}}$$

$$(6\text{-}1)$$

The function on the right-hand side of this equation is the transfer function $T(\omega)$ of the network. In a particular case, if

$$L^2 + C^2 R_L^2 R_g^2 = 2LCR_L^2$$

the coefficient of ω^2 is zero. The transfer function then becomes

$$|T(\omega)| = \frac{R_L/(R_L + R_g)}{\sqrt{1 + \frac{\omega^4 L^2 C^2 R_L^2}{(R_L + R_g)^2}}} \qquad (6\text{-}2)$$

This is a special case of a low-pass filter of the class having transfer functions of the form

$$|T(\omega)| = \frac{A}{\sqrt{1 + (\omega/\omega_0)^{2n}}} \qquad (6\text{-}3)$$

where A and ω_0 are constants depending on the network elements, and n is the number of reactive elements in the network. Such filters are known as *maximally flat,* because the first $2n - 1$ derivatives with respect to frequency are zero at zero frequency; this gives the most nearly constant amplitude response, in the pass-band, that is obtainable with a filter containing n reactive elements. The curve of Fig. 6-5 is of this type.

The transfer function tells us what the response, as a function of frequency, will be when the input is constant with frequency. It is expressed in this form because the reactances of network elements are known in terms of frequency, and it is then easy to analyze a network of such elements in terms of frequency. However, we usually require to find the response, as a function of time, for a given input which is also a function of time.

Now, we saw in Chapter 3 that any function of time can be expressed as a frequency spectrum by Fourier analysis. If $E(\omega)$ is the function of frequency so obtained from the $e(t)$ of Fig. 6-6, $E(\omega)$ is called the *Fourier transform* of $e(t)$, and is related to it by equation 3-26, where $E(\omega)$ replaces $g(\omega)$ and $e(t)$ replaces $f(t)$. At a particular frequency, the input $E(\omega)$ multiplied by the network transfer function $T(\omega)$ gives the output $R(\omega)$. This is true for all frequencies, so that in general

$$R(\omega) = E(\omega) \cdot T(\omega) \qquad (6\text{-}4)$$

The response function $r(t)$ is now obtained as the *inverse Fourier transform* of $R(\omega)$; this is given by equation 3-25, with $R(\omega)$ replacing $g(\omega)$ and $r(t)$ replacing $f(t)$.

To summarize, the response of a given network to a given input is found as follows:

(1) Obtain the Fourier transform of the input function (this is usually not difficult, since the transforms of a large number of functions are listed in mathematics books).

(2) Multiply this by the transfer function.

(3) Take the inverse Fourier transform of the product.

§ 77. As an example, let us consider the application of a square pulse to a low-pass filter. The square pulse is illustrated in Fig. 6-8(a), and the amplitude of its Fourier transform, which is $(\Delta t/2) \cdot \sin(\omega \Delta t/2)/(\omega \Delta t/2)$, is shown in Fig. 6-8(b). The frequency

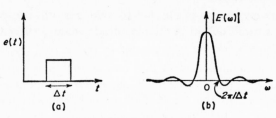

FIG. 6-8   Square pulse

response is the product of this with the transfer function of Fig. 6-5, i.e.,

$$|R(\omega)| \propto \frac{\sin(\omega\Delta t/2)}{\omega\sqrt{1 + (\omega/\omega_0)^{2n}}} \qquad (6\text{-}5)$$

The inverse Fourier transform of this then gives the response as a function of time. The result is illustrated in Fig. 6-9. The greater the bandwidth of the filter, i.e., the greater ω_0, the better approximation is obtained to the original square pulse, but there is always an overshoot. It is possible to design networks which do not give an overshoot, but these are not maximally flat. The beginning and end of the square pulse may be regarded as step functions; similarly, the edge E in Fig. 4-17(a) may be regarded as a step function, and the response in Fig. 4-17(b) is similar to Fig. 6-9.

The frequency response, given by equation 6-5, is a product of the functions illustrated in Figs. 6-5 and 6-8(b). Its form depends on the relative values of $\pi/\Delta t$ and ω_0. If $\omega_0 \gg \pi/\Delta t$, the filter may be regarded as virtually an *all-pass network* (i.e., one which passes all frequencies equally well), and $|R(\omega)|$ is as in Fig. 6-8(b). If $\omega_0 \ll \pi/\Delta t$, the input may be regarded as having an amplitude independent of frequency, and $|R(\omega)|$ is as in Fig. 6-5. Otherwise, $|R(\omega)|$ will

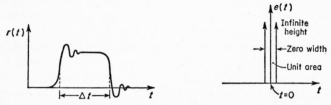

(Left) FIG. 6-9   Response of low-pass filter to square pulse. (Right) FIG. 6-10   Delta function.

be qualitatively similar to Fig. 6-8(b), with zeros in the same positions, and a rapid fall-off of the magnitude when ω exceeds ω_0.

§ 78. Figure 6-8(b) is very similar to Fig. 4-19(a), and the diffraction formula $\sin \beta/\beta$, with $\beta = (\pi a/\lambda) \sin \theta$, may be compared with $\sin (\omega \Delta t/2)/(\omega \Delta t/2)$ obtained above. The formulae are analogous if distance in the screen X, i.e., x, is compared to ω and $(\pi/\lambda) \sin \theta$ to t. Then the screen takes the place of a network in network theory, and a transmitting power may be defined as $P(x)$, equal to zero for $-\infty < x < -a/2$ and for $a/2 < x < \infty$, and to 1 for $-a/2 < x < a/2$. This function is illustrated in Fig. 4-19(b), and is clearly analogous to the transfer function $T(\omega)$ of an ideal lowpass network. Analogous to the transform $E(\omega)$ of the input function $e(t)$ in the network case is the amplitude, as a function of x, of the wavefront, which we may write $A(x)$. The inverse Fourier transform of the product of $A(x)$ and $P(x)$,

$$\psi(\theta) = \frac{1}{\sqrt{2\pi}} \int_{-\infty}^{\infty} A(x) \cdot P(x) \cdot \exp\left[\frac{i\pi x}{\lambda} \sin \theta\right] dx \qquad (6\text{-}6)$$

gives the amplitude distribution of the diffracted wave. For a plane wave, $A(x) = 1$ for all x, and we put $P(x) = 0$ except in the range from $-a/2$ to $+a/2$. Then

$$\psi(\theta) = \frac{1}{\sqrt{2\pi}} \int_{-a/2}^{a/2} \exp\left[\frac{i\pi x}{\lambda} \sin \theta\right] dx \qquad (6\text{-}7)$$

Putting $(\pi x/\lambda) \sin \theta = \beta$, this works out to give

$$\psi(\theta) = \frac{1}{a} \frac{\sin \beta}{\beta} \qquad (6\text{-}8)$$

as before.

The function $A(x)$ may be regarded as the Fourier transform of an input function $a(\varphi)$, where $\varphi = (\pi/\lambda) \sin \theta$, and $a(\varphi)$ may be compared to $e(t)$ in the network case. Physically, $a(\varphi)$ is the polar diagram of the wave which is incident on the diffracting obstacle. Now, the function $A(x) = 1$ for all x, which we have used above, corresponds to $E(\omega) = 1$ for all ω, and this is the Fourier transform of a *delta function*, i.e., $e(t)$ is zero for all t except $t = 0$, where $e(t)$ is infinite (Fig. 6-10). Further, the area enclosed is 1. Similarly, $a(\varphi)$ is zero everywhere except for $\varphi = 0$; this expresses the physical fact that the ray paths are all in the same direction for a plane wave. This example is, perhaps, trivial, but it can be seen that Fourier transform theory provides a link between ray paths and wavefronts, i.e., between geometrical optics and the Huyghens theory.

In the theory of microwave aerials, P and A are functions of both x and y, and the theory is extended to two dimensions. P is usually 1 over a certain area—the aperture of the aerial—and zero elsewhere. A is now not a constant, but a function depending on the way in which the aperture is illuminated. The polar diagram is obtained from the two-dimensional analogue of equation 6-7.

§ 79. Finally, Fourier transform theory can be used to demonstrate the uncertainty principle of wave mechanics. Let us consider a train of waves whose leading edge passes a given point at time t_1, and whose trailing edge passes the point at time t_2. Outside the interval t_1 to t_2, let the amplitude be zero, and in the interval let the wave have constant amplitude, and frequency $\omega_0/2\pi$. Then we have $e(t) = \sin \omega_0 t$ for $t_1 < t < t_2$, and 0 at all other times. The Fourier transform of $e(t)$ gives

$$|E(\omega)| = \frac{\Delta t}{4} \frac{\sin \frac{1}{2}(\omega - \omega_0)\Delta t}{\frac{1}{2}(\omega - \omega_0)\Delta t} \qquad (6\text{-}9)$$

where $\Delta t = t_2 - t_1$, and this is seen to be of the form of Fig. 6-8(b). $E(\omega)$ will be small except in the range of values of ω about ω_0 between the values given by $\frac{1}{2}(\omega - \omega_0)\Delta t = \pm\pi/2$, i.e., in the range $\omega_0 - \pi/\Delta t$ to $\omega_0 + \pi/\Delta t$. Thus we may define

$$\Delta\omega \sim (\omega_0 + \pi/\Delta t) - (\omega_0 - \pi/\Delta t) = 2\pi/\Delta t$$

i.e.,

$$\Delta\omega \cdot \Delta t \sim 2\pi \qquad (6\text{-}10)$$

This is the fundamental uncertainty relationship, and we shall now consider a few of its physical manifestations. Firstly, if a variable resonator is used to measure a frequency ω_0, it will respond if it is tuned to a frequency in the range $\Delta\omega$ about a central frequency ω_0. It is only possible to observe that the frequency under examination is equal to ω_0 if time is allowed for the transient response of the resonator to die away. This time is Δt, given by equation 6-10. Now, the "Q" of the resonator is $\omega_0/\Delta\omega$ (see equation 3-9), so that

$$\frac{\omega_0}{Q}\Delta t \sim 2\pi \quad \text{or} \quad \Delta t \sim 2\pi Q/\omega_0 = Q\tau$$

where τ is the periodic time of oscillation. Thus for the natural frequency of a resonator to establish itself, it is necessary to wait at least Q cycles after the initial excitation.

The train of waves mentioned above may be a radar pulse directed at an aeroplane. The reflected wave suffers a Doppler frequency shift which enables the plane's velocity to be measured, and the time taken for the pulse to return gives a measure of the plane's position. If the phase velocity of the waves is v, the train has a length $\Delta x = v\Delta t$, and this is the uncertainty of the plane's position. If the velocity of the plane is V, the Doppler shift of frequency is $\omega V/v$, and if ω is uncertain to within $\Delta\omega$, the uncertainty of the velocity measurement is $v\Delta\omega/\omega = \Delta V$. Hence

$$\Delta x\Delta V = v\Delta t \cdot v\Delta\omega/\omega = 2\pi v^2/\omega$$

For example, if the frequency is 10^{10} cycles per second, v is $3\cdot10^{10}$ cm/sec, and an accuracy of 3 km/sec $= 3\cdot10^5$ cm/sec is required in the estimate of V, then x is uncertain to $3\cdot10^5$ cm, i.e., 3 km.

This estimate is unduly pessimistic because in practice it is possible to estimate ω by more refined methods than straightforward comparison with a resonator. The value of ω can be determined by observing the shape of a sine curve for only a fraction of a cycle. At the atomic level, however, analogues of these refined radar techniques do not exist, and the fundamental uncertainty cannot be overcome.

The train of waves mentioned at the beginning of this section may be considered to be those associated with a moving electron or other small particle (§ 12). If p is the momentum of the particle, the wavelength is $\lambda = h/p$, where h is Planck's constant. In equation 6-10, write $\omega = 2\pi v/\lambda$ and hence

$$\Delta\omega = 2\pi v\Delta(1/\lambda) = 2\pi v\Delta(p/h) = \frac{2\pi v}{h}\Delta p$$

Therefore

$$\Delta\omega\Delta t = \frac{2\pi}{h}\Delta p \cdot v\Delta t$$

and $v\Delta t$ is the length of the wave train, Δx. Therefore

$$\Delta\omega\Delta t = \frac{2\pi}{h}\,\Delta p\Delta x$$

and this is of order 2π. Hence

$$\Delta p\Delta x \sim h \qquad\qquad (6\text{-}11)$$

which is the form in which the uncertainty relation was first given by Heisenberg. This states that the uncertainty in the momentum of a particle, multiplied by the uncertainty in its position, is of order h (at least, for this takes no account of errors in the measuring instruments themselves), so that inevitably the more accurately either p or x is measured, the less accurately can the other quantity be simultaneously measured. This is clearly analogous to the above case of measuring the position and velocity of an aircraft by means of a single radar pulse.

§ 80. Having discussed some of the things that can be done with wave filters, let us now consider how these things are done in practice.

Fig. 6-7 shows a simple low-pass filter. The response of this filter is not very good, because it is not very flat in the pass-band ($\omega < \omega_0$), and the cut-off is not sharp enough for most purposes, i.e., the response is still appreciable for values of ω above, but not too far above, ω_0. An improved response is given by increasing the number of elements in the filter, as in Fig. 6-11, which shows a *ladder network*

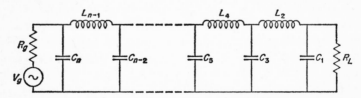

FIG. 6-11   Low-pass ladder network.

with n elements. Fig. 6-7 shows a special case of this, with $n = 2$. The nth element may be a capacity, as in Fig. 6-11, or an inductance, as in Fig. 6-7. The greater n, the flatter the response and the sharper the cut-off, as may be seen from equation 6-3.

The performance of this network may be understood physically by considering it in terms of potential dividers. For this purpose,

it is convenient to redraw the circuit as in Fig. 6-12, for the case
$n = 5$. Between D and earth is a low reactance, $1/\omega C_5$, at high
frequencies, and a high reactance at low frequencies, so that the
voltage V_D at D is high at low frequencies, the voltage drop across
R_g being small, while at high frequencies V_D is low and most of the
generator voltage is developed across R_g, i.e., there is a large voltage
drop in the generator, and the terminal voltage is small.

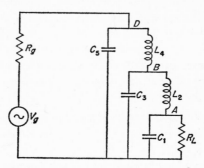

**FIG. 6-12   The network of Fig. 6-11, for $n = 5$, viewed as a number
of potential dividers.**

Of V_D, most is developed across L_4 and little across C_3 at high
frequencies because $\omega L_4 \gg 1/\omega C_3$, while at low frequencies
$\omega L_4 \ll 1/\omega C_3$ and most of V_D appears at B. For ω just above ω_0,
V_B is substantially less than V_D, while for ω just below ω_0, it is
greater. The reason for this is that the circuit consisting of C_3, L_2, C_1
and R_L appears capacitive at low frequencies, and, with L_4, constitutes a resonant circuit, regarding C_5 as contained in the generator.
Thus, as we saw in § 26, V_B can, near ω_0, swing over a wider range
than V_D, and so may be greater than V_D. Above ω_0, the circuit C_3, L_2,
C_1, R_L, appears inductive, and with L_4 constitutes a potential divider
across V_D. The voltage at B is then necessarily less than V_D. Thus
V_B is maximally flat to a higher degree than V_D. Similarly, V_A,
the load voltage, is flatter and cuts off more sharply than V_B.

§ 81. A *band-pass filter* may be obtained by replacing C_1, C_3, C_5,
etc., with parallel tuned circuits, tuned to a frequency ω_0, and replacing L_2, L_4, etc., with series tuned circuits tuned to the same
frequency, as in Fig. 6-13. The parallel circuits present high im-

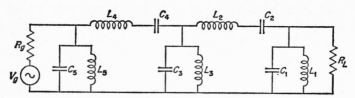

FIG. 6-13   Band-pass ladder network.

pedances at frequencies near ω_0 and low impedances at more distant frequencies, while the series circuits present low impedances at frequencies near ω_0 and high impedances at other frequencies. Thus the response of the circuit of Fig. 6-13 near ω_0 is similar to that of the circuit of Fig. 6-11 at zero frequency, and at other frequencies is similar to the response of the circuit of Fig. 6-11 at high frequencies. Thus the response is as sketched in Fig. 6-4.

§ 82. The flat response of a maximally flat filter in the pass-band causes it to pass a signal containing many different frequencies without distortion. To ensure that signals with nearby frequencies do not enter the receiver, a sharp cut-off is necessary; this may necessitate a large number of circuit elements, making a bulky filter. It is desirable to keep the number of elements in a filter to a minimum, not only because of the cost of the elements, but also because of the increased difficulty of making final adjustments to achieve the desired performance and because of the way the filter itself fits geometrically into the system of which it is a part—an extra coil or condenser may make the difference between being able or unable to put a filter on the same chassis as the rest of the system to which it belongs. The number of elements may be reduced,

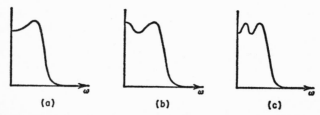

FIG. 6-14   Transfer functions of Chebyshev low-pass filters having (a) two, (b) three, (c) four network elements.

while still obtaining a sharp cut-off, at the cost of a slight distortion in the pass-band. This is done by slightly altering the values of the L's and C's in a certain way. For example, with this design the coefficient of ω^2 in equation 6-1 would no longer be zero. Such filters are known as *Chebyshev filters* because Chebyshev polynomials are used in their design. Typical Chebyshev transfer functions are illustrated in Fig. 6-14.

§ 83. At microwave frequencies, *irises* and *posts* in waveguides behave as inductances, capacities, or as combinations of these. Fig. 6-15 shows an *inductive iris* and a *capacitive iris*. With suitable values

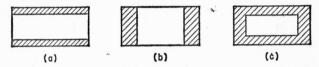

(a)   (b)   (c)

FIG. 6-15   Irises in a waveguide: (a) capacitive, (b) inductive, (c) resonant.

for the dimensions, Fig. 6-15(c) represents a *resonant iris*. The *equivalent circuits* of these are shown in Fig. 6-16; they consist of a length of transmission line, a two-port network, and another length of line.

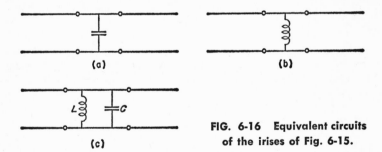

(a)   (b)

(c)

FIG. 6-16   Equivalent circuits of the irises of Fig. 6-15.

The resonant iris illustrated appears as a high impedance near the frequency $\omega = \omega_0 = 1/\sqrt{LC}$, and at this frequency the guide behaves as if there were no iris present. At other frequencies, the iris appears as a low impedance, and the guide behaves like a short-circuited line.

Microwave filter circuits can be made by inserting obstacles of various kinds in the guide at suitable intervals. Fig. 6-17 shows a

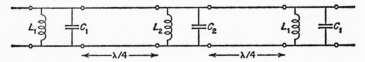

FIG. 6-17 Maximally flat microwave band-pass filter, using resonant irises or posts in a waveguide, each being separated from the next by a quarter-wavelength.

maximally flat filter, consisting of three resonant irises separated by quarter-wavelengths of line. The three resonant circuits are tuned to the same frequency ω_0, but the L-C ratios are chosen differently so that the center circuit gives twice the reflection coefficient of the others at $\omega = \omega_0$. Thus at ω_0 the system gives binomial matching, thereby minimizing the reflection in the pass-band.

§ 84. Acoustic and mechanical filter circuits can be made which work in the same way as electrical lumped-constant or waveguide filters. A common type of mechanical filter consists of a rod of metal, which may be, say, half an inch to two inches or so in length. The radius of this rod changes discontinuously at various points along its length. It is set vibrating in its lowest torsional mode. Typical operating frequencies are in the tens or hundreds of kilocycles per second, and at these frequencies the wavelength is less than the rod length, so that it behaves as the mechanical analogue of a transmission line. The different radii correspond to different characteristic impedances, and reflection occurs at the discontinuities. By suitably designing the magnitudes and separations between discontinuities, filters can be made, analogously to interference filters (§ 24). These filters are much less bulky than lumped-constant electric filters and are replacing them to a large extent in electronic circuits.

The loudspeaker and the various elements of the cabinet in which it is mounted constitute an acoustic filter in the case of a radio set. Ideally, the output from the final amplification stage of the receiver should be converted into sound waves without modification, so that the acoustic set-up should perform as an all-pass filter. In practice, it will behave as a low-pass filter, and the cut-off frequency must be as high as possible. The various elements appear to sound waves as short sections of transmission line, and so may be regarded as inductances and capacities. The design problem is made more difficult by the fact that the inductance and capacity vary with frequency, since the effective length of a line is frequency-dependent.

Symbols Used in This Book

The following symbols are used throughout this book with the meanings indicated. Occasional use of these symbols with different meanings, or of other symbols, also occurs, and the definitions are given at the appropriate places.

A, a, a'	Amplitude
a	Slit width or aperture width
a, b	Dimensions of rectangular membrane or waveguide
c	Velocity of light
C	Capacity in AC circuit, or capacity per unit length of a transmission line
d	Linear distance, or skin depth
E	Electric field or Young's Modulus
$e(t)$	Input function (to a network)
$E(\omega)$	Fourier transform of $e(t)$
g	Acceleration due to gravity
h	Planck's constant
H	Magnetic field
I	Electric current
j	Square root of -1
k	Quantity which occurs, multiplied by a relevant dimension, in a wave function; the value of the product has to be chosen so that the wave function satisfies the boundary conditions
l	Length of a string, pendulum, or transmission line
L	Inductance in AC circuits, or inductance per unit length of a transmission line
m	Mass
m, n	Integers
n	Rigidity modulus

P	Pressure of a gas
Q	Quantity expressing the sharpness of a resonance curve
r, R	Reflection coefficient
R	Resistance of an electrical circuit
$r(t)$	Response function of a network
$R(\omega)$	Fourier transform of $r(t)$
s	Linear distance
t	Time
t, T	Transmission coefficient
$T(\omega)$	Transfer function of a network
T	Surface tension of water or tension of a string
V	Electric potential
v	Wave velocity
$v\phi$	Phase velocity
v_g	Group velocity
W	Energy
x, y	Distance
Y	Admittance of an AC circuit
Z	Impedance of an AC circuit
Z_0	Characteristic impedance of a transmission line
z	Distance in the direction of propagation of a wave
α	Phase angle or attenuation constant
β	Phase constant
ϵ	Permittivity or dielectric constant
θ	Phase angle
κ	Elastic modulus of a cord or bulk modulus of a liquid
λ	Wavelength
μ	Refractive index or relative permeability
ν	Frequency
ξ	Displacement
ρ	Radial distance or density
σ	Conductivity
φ	Phase
ψ	Wave function in wave mechanics, such that $|\psi|^2$ is a probability or probability density
ω	2π times frequency
Ω	2π times modulating frequency

Bibliography

The following are recommended for further general reading about waves.

J. A. Fleming, *Waves and Ripples in Water, Air, and Aether*, London, Society for Promoting Christian Knowledge, 1912.

H. S. Stewart, "The New Optics," *International Science and Technology*, No. 4, pp. 15–26 (April 1962).

R. A. Frosch, "Underwater Sound," *International Science and Technology*, No. 9, pp. 40–46 (September 1962).

B. Vesey-Fitzgerald, "The Senses of Bats," *Endeavour*, Vol. 6, pp. 36–41 (1947).

G. E. R. Deacon, "Ocean Waves," *Endeavour*, Vol. 17, pp. 134–139 (July 1958).

W. H. Bragg, *The Universe of Light*, London, Bell, 1933.

G. E. Duvall, "Shock Waves in Solids," *International Science and Technology*, No. 16, pp. 45-52 (April 1963).

R. C. H. Russell and D. H. MacMillan, *Waves and Tides*, London, Hutchinson, 1952.

I. Dyer, "Statistical Vibration Analysis," *International Science and Technology*, No. 20, pp. 35-41 (August 1963).

C. C. Cutler, "Coherent Light," *International Science and Technology*, No. 21, pp. 54-63 (September 1963).

J. King *et al.*, "Infrared," *International Science and Technology*, No. 16, pp. 26-37 (April 1963).

B. L. Walsh, "Parametric Amplification," *International Science and Technology*, No. 17, pp. 75-81 (May 1963).

B. R. Brinley, "The Maser," *The Microwave Journal*, Vol. 5, pp. 86-94 (August 1962).

G. W. Swenson, *Principles of Modern Acoustics*, Princeton, Van Nostrand, 1953.

G. B. Welch, *Wave Propagation and Antennas*, Princeton, Van Nostrand, 1958.

The following two books are written at a sophisticated mathematical level, but should be studied by anyone interested in waves who knows enough mathematics to do so.

C. A. Coulson, *Waves*, Oliver and Boyd, London, Interscience Publishers New York, 1952.

A. R. von Hippel, *Dielectrics and Waves*, New York, John Wiley, 1954.

Index